TEACHER EDITION • Chapter 11
Geometry and Fraction Concepts

Houghton Mifflin Harcourt

S0-BND-556

Copyright © 2015 by Houghton Mifflin Harcourt Publishing Company

All rights reserved. No part of this work may be reproduced or transmitted in any form or by any means, electronic or mechanical, including photocopying or recording, or by any information storage and retrieval system, without the prior written permission of the copyright owner unless such copying is expressly permitted by federal copyright law. Requests for permission to make copies of any part of the work should be addressed to Houghton Mifflin Harcourt Publishing Company, Attn: Contracts, Copyrights, and Licensing, 9400 Southpark Center Loop, Orlando, Florida 32819-8647.

Common Core State Standards © Copyright 2010. National Governors Association Center for Best Practices and Council of Chief State School Officers. All rights reserved.

This product is not sponsored or endorsed by the Common Core State Standards Initiative of the National Governors Association Center for Best Practices and the Council of Chief State School Officers.

Printed in the U.S.A.

ISBN 978-0-544-29586-5

5 6 7 8 9 10 0029 22 21 20 19 18 17 16 15
4500541314   B C D E F G

If you have received these materials as examination copies free of charge, Houghton Mifflin Harcourt Publishing Company retains title to the materials and they may not be resold. Resale of examination copies is strictly prohibited.

Possession of this publication in print format does not entitle users to convert this publication, or any portion of it, into electronic format.

© Houghton Mifflin Harcourt Publishing Company • Cover Image Credits: (Goosander) ©Erich Kuchling/ Westend61/Corbis; (Covered bridge, New Hampshire) ©eye35/Alamy Images

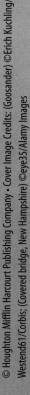

Critical Area — Geometry and Fractions

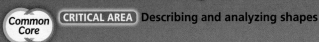

Common Core · **CRITICAL AREA** Describing and analyzing shapes

Table of Contents

Chapter 11 Geometry and Fraction Concepts

Domain:

Geometry   2.G

* This chapter also includes the following standard: 2.OA.C.4

Common Core MATHEMATICAL PRACTICES

MP1 Make sense of problems and persevere in solving them.

MP2 Reason abstractly and quantitatively.

MP3 Construct viable arguments and critique the reasoning of others.

MP4 Model with mathematics.

MP5 Use appropriate tools strategically.

MP6 Attend to precision.

MP7 Look for and make use of structure.

MP8 Look for and express regularity in repeated reasoning.

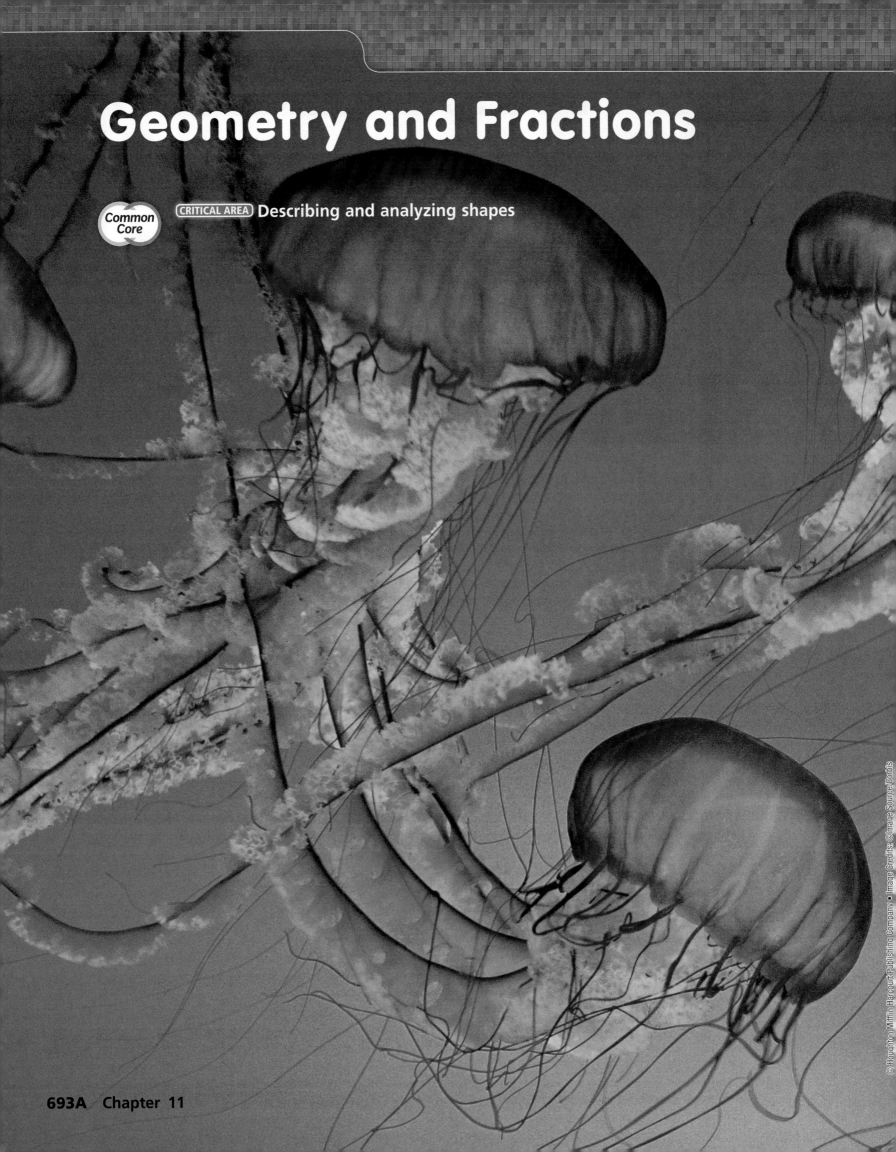

Geometry and Fractions

Common Core (CRITICAL AREA) Describing and analyzing shapes

© Houghton Mifflin Harcourt Publishing Company • Image Credits: ©Image Source/Corbis

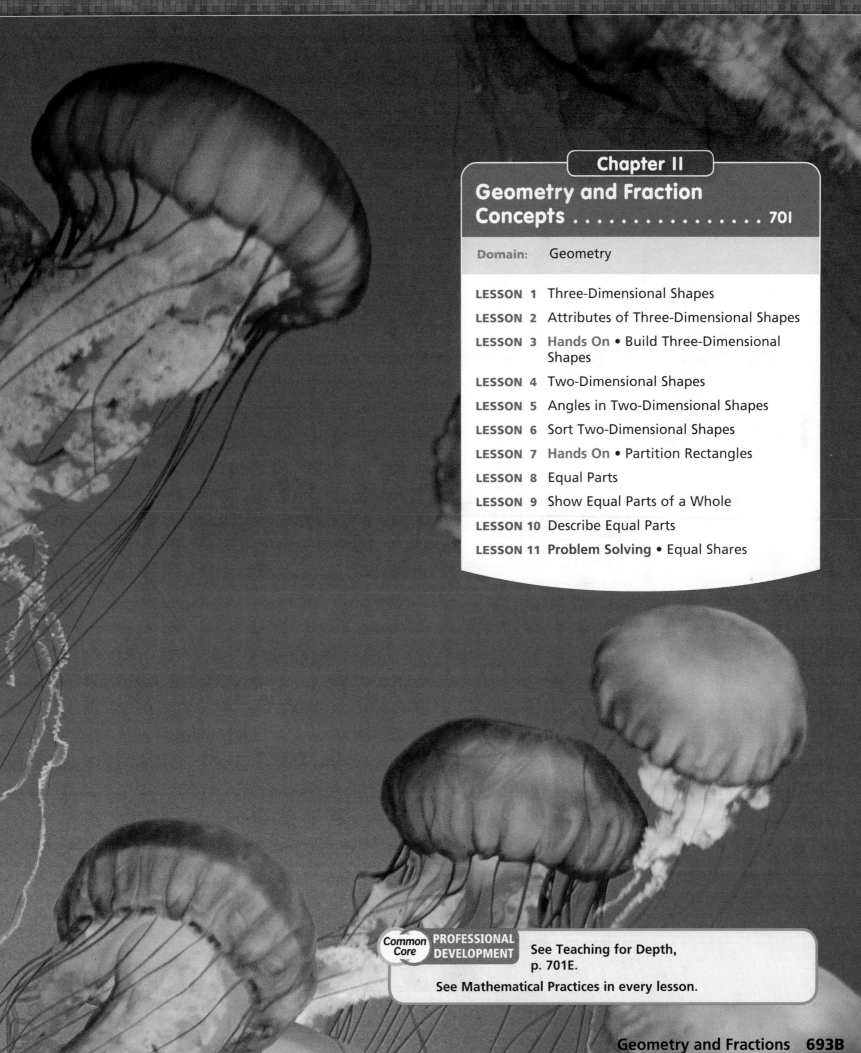

Common Core **PROFESSIONAL DEVELOPMENT**

See Teaching for Depth, p. 701E.

See Mathematical Practices in every lesson.

Digital Resources

FOR LEARNING...

Interactive Student Edition

- Immerses students in an interactive, multi-sensory math environment
- Enhances learning with scaffolded, interactive instruction and just-in-time feedback
- Provides audio reinforcement for each lesson
- Makes learning a two-way experience, using a variety of interactive tools

FOR ASSESSMENT AND INTERVENTION...

Personal Math Trainer

- Creates a personalized learning path for each student
- Provides opportunities for practice, homework, and assessment
- Includes worked-out examples and helpful video support
- Offers targeted intervention and extra support to build proficiency and understanding

FOR DAILY MATH TUTORING...

Math on the Spot Videos

- Models good problem-solving thinking in every lesson
- Engages students through interesting animations and fun characters
- Builds student problem-solving proficiency and confidence
- Builds the skills needed for success on the Common Core assessments

© Houghton Mifflin Harcourt Publishing Company •
Image Credits: (tr) ©Comstock/Getty Images

⏻ Interactive Teacher Digital Management Center

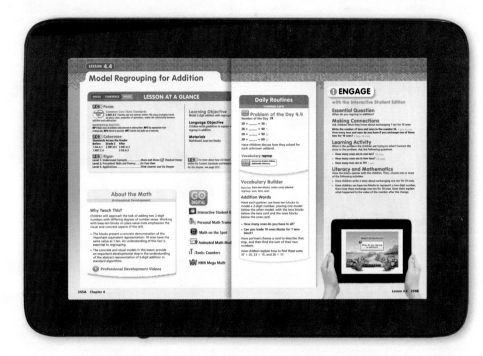

Teacher Edition

• Plan your lessons from the convenience of your classroom, at home, or on the go

• View student lessons 24/7

• Access *Math on the Spot* videos anytime, anywhere

• Offers Common Core-specific learning and instructional activities and suggestions

Professional Development Videos

• Learn more about the Common Core and Common Core content

• See first-hand the integration of the Mathematical Practices

• Watch students engaged in a productive struggle

Digital Resource Management System

• Manage online all program content and components

• Search for and select resources based on Common Core standards

• Identify resources based on student ability and needs

• View and assign student lessons, practice, assessments, and more

© Houghton Mifflin Harcourt Publishing Company • Image Credits: (b) ©Comstock/Getty Images

① READ

A Farmer's Job

Objective Use literature to review and reinforce geometry concepts.

Genre Nonfiction

Domain: Geometry

▶ **Preparing to Read** Refer children to the story cover and read the title. Have children talk about what happens on a farm. Explain that together they will read a story about a farmer's job and identify shapes shown in the pictures. Then they will read the story again and learn fun facts to answer social studies questions about the story.

▶ **Story Vocabulary** season, fruits, vegetables, plow, fertilize, soil, seeds, crops, weather, harvest

▶ **Reading the Math Story**
Pages 693–696

The story tells the jobs a farmer does each season.

• **What shapes make up the barn?** Possible answers: triangle, rectangle, rectangular prism

• **Which shapes do you see on the truck?** Possible answers: rectangle, rectangular prism

Vocabulary Reader · Critical Area · Geometry and Fractions

A Farmer's Job
by Tami Morton

Common Core · CRITICAL AREA · Describing and analyzing shapes

693

A farmer's job is never done. Farmers are busy during all of the seasons of the year. They grow fruits and vegetables for people to eat. What shapes do you see?

Some possible answers: triangle, rectangle, rectangular prism

694   Why is a farmer's work important?

In the spring, farmers get the fields ready. They plow the fields and fertilize the soil. They plant their seeds. What shapes do you see?

Some possible answers: rectangle, rectangular prism

How is a farmer's work today different from long ago?   695

In the summer, farmers take care of their crops. They make sure that the plants have enough water when it does not rain. What shapes do you see?

Some possible answers: cone, cylinder, rectangle, circle

696   Why does a farmer need to know about changes in the weather?

In the fall, farmers harvest many fruits and vegetables. They sell most of these fruits and vegetables to other people.

What shapes do you see?

Some possible answers: sphere, cylinder, circle

Why does a farmer grow more fruits and vegetables than his or her family can eat? **697**

In the winter, farmers clear the fields and get ready for the next season.
They plan what they are going to plant.
They check their machines.
A farmer's job is never done.

What shapes do you see?
Some possible answers: cylinder, cone, rectangular prism, rectangle

698 Why are the seasons important to a farmer?

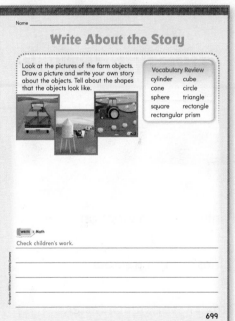

Name _____

Write About the Story

Look at the pictures of the farm objects. Draw a picture and write your own story about the objects. Tell about the shapes that the objects look like.

Vocabulary Review
cylinder   cube
cone   circle
sphere   triangle
square   rectangle
rectangular prism

WRITE ▸ Math
Check children's work.

699

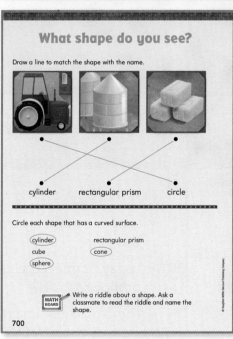

What shape do you see?

Draw a line to match the shape with the name.

cylinder   rectangular prism   circle

Circle each shape that has a curved surface.

cylinder   rectangular prism
cube   cone
sphere

MATH BOARD Write a riddle about a shape. Ask a classmate to read the riddle and name the shape.

700

Pages 697 and 698

Children should understand the story progression.

- **Which objects in the pictures are shaped like rectangular prisms?** Possible answer: hay bales
- **Which shapes do you see on the towers?** Possible answers: cones and cylinders

2 RESPOND

Write About the Story

Page 699

WRITE ▸ Math Ask children to look at the pictures of farm objects. Encourage children to use the review vocabulary in their stories. Ask volunteers to share their stories with the class.

▶ **Math Vocabulary** cylinder, cone, sphere, square, rectangular prism, cube, circle, triangle, rectangle

Do the Math

- **What shape do you see?**

Page 700

In this activity, children practice identifying shapes. Then they write a riddle about a shape.

Connections to Social Studies

Read the story again as children follow along. Then read aloud the fun facts about farming listed below. Have children look at the story pictures and discuss the Social Studies question on each page.

Food Facts:

- Most of our food comes from farmers.

- Farmers grow many fruits and vegetables on their farms.

- They grow corn, wheat, tomatoes, strawberries, and other foods we eat every day.

Farming Facts:

- Long ago, farmers used animals to do work on the farm.

- Today, farmers use machines such as tractors or plows.

- These machines make farmers' work much faster.

Water Facts:

- Farmers pay attention to the weather so their crops will grow.

- If it does not rain enough, farmers must water the plants.

- They can use sprinklers or dig canals to bring water to the plants.

Farmer Facts:

- Usually, a farmer grows just a few kinds of crops.

- The farmer sells these crops to people for money.

- The farmer uses the money to buy other foods and items for his or her family.

Season Facts:

- Each season, different work needs to be done on the farm.

- The crops grow best if the seeds are planted at a certain time of year.

- The farmer also needs to know the best season to harvest the crops

Real World Project

© Houghton Mifflin Harcourt Publishing Company

Some people make quilts to sell.
Here is a pretty quilt at the stand.

Red		Red
Orange		Orange
Blue	Orange	Blue

Color the squares blue.

Color the triangles red.

Color the rectangles orange.

B7

Page 4

At the Farm Stand

My Pictures

A Math Storybook

by _____

CRITICAL AREA Describing and analyzing shapes

Sunshine Farm Stand sells many things.
Look at the picture.

Draw an X in the circle.
Draw stripes in the squares.
Draw dots in the triangle.
Draw a door in the rectangle.

X

dots

SUNSHINE FARM STAND

stripes   door   stripes

Page 2

© Houghton Mifflin Harcourt Publishing Company

There are many yummy things for sale.

GRAPE JELLY   CHEESE

SOUP   CRACKERS

How many ⬚ do you see?

_2_ cylinders

How many ⬚ do you see?

_1_ spheres

How many ⬚ do you see?

_2_ rectangular prisms

Page 3

B8

My Math Project Storybook

At the Farm Stand

Objective Develop understanding of geometry concepts.

Genre Nonfiction

Print and copy the pages from the Online Projects and help children fold them to make their own storybooks. Explain that they will work together to complete stories about things that are found at a farm stand.

On page 2 of the storybook, children identify the shapes they see. Have them describe what circles, squares, triangles, and rectangles look like to help them complete the activity. On page 3, children identify the three-dimensional shape they see and tell how many of each shape they see. Ask children to tell which objects have a similar shape. On page 4, children color some of the two-dimensional shapes shown in a quilt pattern.

After children have completed the pages, have them share their work with the class, and then take their storybooks home to share with family members.

Performance Assessment You may suggest that children place completed projects in their portfolios.

Chapter At A Glance
Domain: Geometry

Chapter Essential Question What are some two-dimensional shapes and three-dimensional shapes, and how can you show equal parts of shapes?

Use the *Go Math! Planning Guide* for correlations, math practices information, and more.

1 Day	**1 Day**	**1 Day**
LESSON 11.1 2.G.A.1	**LESSON 11.2** 2.G.A.1	**LESSON 11.3** 2.G.A.1

Lesson At A Glance

	Three-Dimensional Shapes 705A	**Attributes of Three-Dimensional Shapes** 711A	**Hands On • Build Three-Dimensional Shapes** 717A
Essential Question	What objects match three-dimensional shapes?	How would you describe the faces of a rectangular prism and the faces of a cube?	How can you build a rectangular prism?
Objective	Identify three-dimensional shapes.	Identify and describe three-dimensional shapes according to the number of faces, edges, and vertices.	Build three-dimensional shapes using cubes and other objects.
Vocabulary	cube, rectangular prism, sphere, cylinder, cone	face, edge, vertex, vertices	
ELL Strategy	**ELL** Strategy • Illustrate Understanding	**ELL** Strategy • Restate	**ELL** Strategy • Scaffold Language

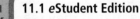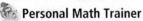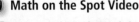

GO DIGITAL Go online to access all your chapter resources

www.thinkcentral.com

11.1 *eStudent Edition*	11.2 *eStudent Edition*	11.3 *eStudent Edition*
11.1 *eTeacher Edition*	11.2 *eTeacher Edition*	11.3 *eTeacher Edition*
Personal Math Trainer	Personal Math Trainer	Personal Math Trainer
Math on the Spot Video	Math on the Spot Video	Math on the Spot Video
Animated Math Models	*iTools*	
iTools	HMH Mega Math	
HMH Mega Math		

Print Resources

11.1 Student Edition	**11.2 Student Edition**	**11.3 Student Edition**
11.1 Practice and Homework (in the *Student Edition*)	**11.2 Practice and Homework** (in the *Student Edition*)	**11.3 Practice and Homework** (in the *Student Edition*)
11.1 Reteach (in the *Chapter Resources*)	11.2 Reteach (in the *Chapter Resources*)	11.3 Reteach (in the *Chapter Resources*)
11.1 Enrich (in the *Chapter Resources*)	11.2 Enrich (in the *Chapter Resources*)	11.3 Enrich (in the *Chapter Resources*)
Grab-and-Go™ Centers Kit	Grab-and-Go™ Centers Kit	Grab-and-Go™ Centers Kit

Before the Chapter	During the Lesson	After the Chapter
✔ **Show What You Know**	✔ **Share and Show**	✔ **Chapter Review/Test**
• Prerequisite Skills Activities • Personal Math Trainer	• RtI Tier 1 Lesson (online) • Mid-Chapter Checkpoint • Personal Math Trainer	• RtI Tier 1 Lesson (online) • Personal Math Trainer

RtI Response to Intervention

I Day

LESSON II.4 **2.G.A.I**

Two-Dimensional Shapes 723A

What shapes can you name just by knowing the number of sides and vertices?

Name 3-, 4-, 5-, and 6-sided shapes according to the number of sides and vertices.

side, vertex, vertices, quadrilateral, pentagon, hexagon

ELL Strategy • Illustrate Understanding

I Day

LESSON II.5 **2.G.A.I**

Angles in Two-Dimensional Shapes 729A

How do you find and count angles in two-dimensional shapes?

Identify angles in two-dimensional shapes.

angle, quadrilateral, pentagon, triangle, rectangle

ELL Strategy • Illustrate Understanding

I Day

LESSON II.6 **2.G.A.I**

Sort Two-Dimensional Shapes 735A

How do you use the number of sides and angles to sort two-dimensional shapes?

Sort two-dimensional shapes according to their attributes.

sides, angles

ELL Strategy • Illustrate Understanding

11.4 *e*Student Edition

11.4 *e*Teacher Edition

Personal Math Trainer

Math on the Spot Video

Animated Math Models

*i*Tools

HMH Mega Math

11.5 *e*Student Edition

11.5 *e*Teacher Edition

Personal Math Trainer

Math on the Spot Video

11.6 *e*Student Edition

11.6 *e*Teacher Edition

Personal Math Trainer

Math on the Spot Video

Animated Math Models

*i*Tools

HMH Mega Math

11.4 Student Edition

11.4 Practice and Homework
(in the *Student Edition*)

11.4 Reteach (in the *Chapter Resources*)

11.4 Enrich (in the *Chapter Resources*)

Grab-and-Go™ Centers Kit

11.5 Student Edition

11.5 Practice and Homework
(in the *Student Edition*)

11.5 Reteach (in the *Chapter Resources*)

11.5 Enrich (in the *Chapter Resources*)

Grab-and-Go™ Centers Kit

11.6 Student Edition

11.6 Practice and Homework
(in the *Student Edition*)

11.6 Reteach (in the *Chapter Resources*)

11.6 Enrich (in the *Chapter Resources*)

Grab-and-Go™ Centers Kit

 Resources *www.thinkcentral.com*

 Interactive Student Edition

Personal Math Trainer

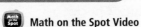 Math on the Spot Video

Animated Math Models

 Assessment

HMH Mega Math

 *i*Tools

Multimedia *e*Glossary

Professional Development Videos

Geometry and Fraction Concepts   701B

Chapter At A Glance

Domain: Geometry

	1 Day **LESSON 11.7** 2.G.A.2	**1 Day** **LESSON 11.8** 2.G.A.3	**1 Day** **LESSON 11.9** Common Core 2.G.A.3
Lesson At A Glance	**Hands On • Partition Rectangles....... 741A**	**Equal Parts......747A**	**Show Equal Parts of a Whole.......... 753A**
Essential Question	How do you find the total number of same-size squares that will cover a rectangle?	What are halves, thirds, and fourths of a whole?	How do you know if a shape shows halves, thirds, or fourths?
Objective	Partition rectangles into equal-size squares and find the total number of these squares.	Identify and name equal parts of circles and rectangles as halves, thirds, or fourths.	Partition shapes to show halves, thirds, or fourths.
Vocabulary	rectangle, rows, columns	halves, thirds, fourths, equal parts, whole	equal parts, whole, halves, thirds, fourths
ELL Strategy	**ELL** Strategy • Scaffold Language	**ELL** Strategy • Cooperative Grouping	**ELL** Strategy • Model Concepts

GO DIGITAL Go online to access all your chapter resources

FPO

www.thinkcentral.com

11.7 *e*Student Edition 11.7 *e*Teacher Edition Personal Math Trainer Math on the Spot Video	11.8 *e*Student Edition 11.8 *e*Teacher Edition Personal Math Trainer Math on the Spot Video HMH Mega Math	11.9 *e*Student Edition 11.9 *e*Teacher Edition Personal Math Trainer Math on the Spot Video 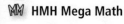 HMH Mega Math

Print Resources		

11.7 Student Edition
11.7 Practice and Homework
   (in the *Student Edition*)
11.7 Reteach (in the *Chapter Resources*)
11.7 Enrich (in the *Chapter Resources*)
Grab-and-Go™ Centers Kit
	11.8 Student Edition
	11.8 Practice and Homework
	   (in the *Student Edition*)
	11.8 Reteach (in the *Chapter Resources*)
	11.8 Enrich (in the *Chapter Resources*)
	Grab-and-Go™ Centers Kit
		11.9 Student Edition
		11.9 Practice and Homework
		   (in the *Student Edition*)
		11.9 Reteach (in the *Chapter Resources*)
		11.9 Enrich (in the *Chapter Resources*)
		Grab-and-Go™ Centers Kit

Assessment

Diagnostic	**Formative**	**Summative**

• **Show What You Know**
• **Diagnostic Interview Task**
• **Digital Personal Math Trainer**
	• **Lesson Quick Check**
	• **Mid-Chapter Checkpoint**
	• **Digital Personal Math Trainer**
	  - *Assessment Animation*
	  - *Assessment Video*
		• **Chapter Review/Test**
		• **Chapter Test**
		• **Performance Assessment Task**
		• **Digital Personal Math Trainer**

| Day

LESSON 11.10 **2.G.A.3**

Describe Equal Parts......... 759A

How do you find a half of, a third of, or a fourth of a whole?

Identify and describe one equal part as a half of, a third of, or a fourth of a whole.

half of, third of, fourth of, quarter of

ELL Strategy • Illustrate Understanding

11.10 *e*Student Edition

11.10 *e*Teacher Edition

Personal Math Trainer

Math on the Spot Video

11.10 Student Edition

11.10 Practice and Homework (in the *Student Edition*)

11.10 Reteach (in the *Chapter Resources*)

11.10 Enrich (in the *Chapter Resources*)

Grab-and-Go™ Centers Kit

|–2 Days

LESSON 11.11 **2.G.A.3**

Problem Solving • Equal Shares 765A

How can drawing a diagram help when solving problems about equal shares?

Solve problems involving wholes divided into equal shares by using the strategy *draw a diagram.*

halves, thirds, fourths

ELL Strategy • Identify Relationships

11.11 *e*Student Edition

11.11 *e*Teacher Edition

Personal Math Trainer

Math on the Spot Video

✓ Chapter 11 Test

11.11 Student Edition

11.11 Practice and Homework (in the *Student Edition*)

11.11 Reteach (in the *Chapter Resources*)

11.11 Enrich (in the *Chapter Resources*)

Grab-and-Go™ Centers Kit

Teacher Notes

PROFESSIONAL DEVELOPMENT

Teaching for Depth

Edward B. Burger, Ph.D.
President, Southwestern University
Georgetown, Texas

Reasoning with Shapes and Their Attributes

Children already have substantial experience with plane, or two-dimensional, figures including naming and sorting them by number of sides or angles. This is extended to include three-dimensional figures, as well as other attributes.

- Children develop fluency in vocabulary when they describe attributes of shapes.

- Children can use various attributes to classify shapes. This helps them develop concepts for different types of shapes.

- Children can also investigate shapes by combining or partitioning them to make new shapes.

- Drawing shapes is a way to support children in developing an understanding of shapes and their attributes. Using dot paper or grid paper helps children learn how to draw shapes.

From the Research

❝Teachers must provide materials and structure the environment to encourage students to explore shapes and their attributes. [Students must] analyze characteristics and properties of two- and three-dimensional geometric shapes and develop mathematical arguments about geometric relationships.❞ (NCTM, 2000, p. 97)

Professional Development Videos:
Measurement and Geometry, Grades K–2, Segments 1 and 2

Reasoning with Shapes and Fractions

The concept of dividing a whole into equal parts is key to understanding and naming fractions.

- Children encounter many situations where they can develop this understanding. Papers are divided in halves, pizzas are divided into equal parts, or cakes are cut fairly.

- Both geometry and fraction concepts can be strengthened by connecting real objects to fair shares.

- These experiences build the foundation for equivalent fractions and the common denominator algorithm that will be learned in later grades.

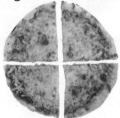

Common Core Mathematical Practices

Children learn to **use appropriate tools strategically** to understand and solve problems dealing with geometry and fractions. They may draw lines to divide shapes into equal parts; use dot paper to help them draw figures; use manipulatives to make shapes; and fold paper into equal sections and accurately name the resulting fractions. These are a few examples of how children learn to select and use suitable tools to explore and enhance their understanding.

Daily Classroom Management

Differentiated Instruction

Whole Group	Small Group	Whole Group
1 ENGAGE	**3** EXPLAIN	**4** ELABORATE
2 EXPLORE	✓ QUICK CHECK	**5** EVALUATE

0 to 1 correct — RtI

INTERVENE
These children need lesson support.

2 correct

ON LEVEL
These children are ready to begin independent practice.

Advanced

ENRICH
These children are ready for enrichment.

Extra Support

Teachers may need to decelerate the rate at which new material is introduced.

- Reteach (in the *Chapter Resources*)
- **ELL** Activity

GO DIGITAL

- Strategic Intervention Guide
- Intensive Intervention Guide
- Personal Math Trainer

On Level

- Practice and Homework (in the *Student Edition*)
- **ELL** Activity

GO DIGITAL

- HMH Mega Math
- *i*Tools

Enrich

Teachers may need to accelerate the rate at which new material is introduced.

- Advanced Learners Activity
- Enrich (in the *Chapter Resources*)
- Extend the Project
- **ELL** Activity

GO DIGITAL

- HMH Mega Math
- *i*Tools

WHAT ARE THE OTHER CHILDREN DOING?

Differentiated Centers Kit

The kit provides literature, games, and activities for use every day.

Strategies for
English Language Learners

by Elizabeth Jiménez
CEO, GEMAS Consulting
Professional Expert on
English Learner Education
Bilingual Education and Dual Language
Pomona, California

The **Illustrate Understanding Strategy** allows English Language Learners to communicate their understanding using little language. Teachers ask children to sketch to communicate their understanding.

Benefit to English Language Learners

Illustrating understanding provides the teacher a visual insight into the children's understanding of a math concept. It is beneficial to English Language Learners because:

- it allows children to communicate their understanding using little language.

- it provides a visual for the child to see and recognize his or her own gaps in understanding.

- all children may express their understanding at the same time.

From the Research

"Drawings and questions are a means of self-monitoring. They also can offer teachers windows into students' thinking and thus provide information about how better to help students along a learning path to efficient problem-solving methods."

How Students Learn: Mathematics in the Classroom; National Research Council.

Planning for Instruction

Not only does the Illustrate Understanding strategy provide a window into the children's thinking, it provides a window for all children at the same time. For example, asking children to draw a triangle, allowing time for them to draw a triangle, and asking them to show the triangle simultaneously provides instant assessment of each child's understanding of a triangle.

Illustrate Understanding is a simple strategy that is easy to use with little to no preparation. You can use the Illustrate Understanding strategy to:

- assess children's understanding of a concept,

- allow children to communicate without language,

- help children create a visual to aid in communicating their ideas, and

- use as samples for children's portfolios for parent conferences.

Encourage children to keep their drawings quick and uncomplicated so that they do not get bogged down with the drawing or intimidated by the quality of drawing. Praise the thinking that is expressed in the drawing rather than the artistic expression of the drawing.

Illustrate Understanding is an excellent way for children of all language abilities to demonstrate their understanding. It can also be used by teachers to enhance comprehension and accessibility of a lesson.

Linguistic Note

Illustrate Understanding is an effective strategy for this chapter focusing on two-dimensional shapes. This strategy allows children to learn and show their understanding with the use of little language. Encourage children, however, to talk about their drawings to build the necessary language skills.

Developing Math Language

Chapter Vocabulary

angle a shape formed by two line segments that share the same endpoint

cone a three-dimensional shape with a circular base and a point at the top

cube a three-dimensional shape with six square faces

cylinder a three-dimensional shape with two circular parallel bases and a curved surface

edge where two faces of a three-dimensional shape meet

face a polygon that is a flat surface of a three-dimensional shape

fourths four equal parts

halves two equal parts

hexagon a polygon with six sides

pentagon a polygon with five sides

quadrilateral a polygon with four sides

rectangular prism a three-dimensional shape with six faces that are rectangles

side one of the line segments that forms a polygon

thirds three equal parts

vertex the point where 2 sides of a polygon meet or 3 or more edges of a three-dimensional shape meet

 GO DIGITAL
- **Interactive Student Edition**
- **Multimedia eGlossary**

ELL Vocabulary Activity

See ELL Activity Guide for leveled activities.

Objective Understand the math term quadrilateral

Materials Vocabulary Card quadrilateral (see *eTeacher Resources*)

Draw a non-square rectangle, a square, a trapezoid, and a rhombus on the board. Then show children the Vocabulary Card for *quadrilateral* and explain that all these shapes are called *quadrilaterals*. Remind children that quadrilaterals have four sides and four vertices. Have a volunteer point out the sides and vertices of the shapes on the board. Discuss how the shapes are alike or different from each other.

Practice vocabulary by using questioning strategies such as:

Beginning
- Point to the square and rectangle on the board. **How are these two shapes alike?** They both have four sides and four vertices.

Intermediate
- Have children find three examples of quadrilaterals in the classroom. Answers will vary.

Advanced
- Have children choose two or more different quadrilaterals and show how to divide them into two equal parts. Check children's work.

Vocabulary Strategy • Word Wall

- On the word wall, post new words and review words that children may need to practice as each lesson is introduced.
- Practice these words as a "warm-up" activity before the lessons.
- When the word appears in the lesson, reinforce it by pointing to it on the word wall.

Add these words to the word wall.

hexagon

cylinder

pentagon

quadrilateral

cube

Review Prerequisite Skills

TIER 2

Turn the Shape!

Objective Recognize shapes shown in various orientations.
Materials square, rectangle, and triangle cutouts to trace; paper

Have children name each shape. Ask them to trace a square. Tell them to move the square to a new place on the paper, turn it a little, and trace it again. Repeat so they have several orientations for the square.

Ask: **Look at the shapes you drew. Which ones are squares?** all of them **Does a shape change if you turn it?** no

Have children repeat with other shapes.

Children can then use the shapes to make a picture. Have them count how many of each shape they used in their picture.

TIER 3

Fold It!

Objective Recognize equal and unequal parts.
Materials cutouts of Plane Shapes (see *eTeacher Resources*), crayons

Use two rectangles to show equal and unequal parts. Give children two cutouts of rectangles. One rectangle has a vertical line drawn through the center, dividing it into two equal parts. The other rectangle has a vertical line drawn near the left side of it, dividing the rectangle into two unequal parts. Have children look at the rectangles.

Ask:

- **How many parts are the rectangles divided into?**
  2 parts

Have children fold the rectangles along the vertical lines.

- **Which rectangle shows equal parts? Explain.** The rectangle with the line down the center shows equal parts. Possible explanation: When I fold that rectangle, the parts are the same size. The parts in the other rectangle are different sizes when I fold it.

Repeat with other shapes, such as squares divided into four equal and unequal parts and circles divided into two equal and unequal parts.

Geometry

Common Core Learning Progressions Across the Grades

Before	Grade 2	After
• Reason with shapes and their attributes.	• Reason with shapes and their attributes.	• Reason with shapes and their attributes.

Common Core State Standards Across the Grades

Before	Grade 2	After
Domain: Geometry Reason with shapes and their attributes. **1.G.A.1, 1.G.A.2, 1.G.A.3**	**Domain: Geometry** Reason with shapes and their attributes. **2.G.A.1, 2.G.A.2, 2.G.A.3**	**Domain: Geometry** Reason with shapes and their attributes. **3.G.A.1, 3.G.A.2**

See A page of each Lesson for Common Core Standard text.

Chapter 11

Introduce the Chapter

Hot air rises. A balloon filled with hot air will float up into the sky.

Some balloons look as though they have two-dimensional shapes on them. Name some two-dimensional shapes. Then draw some examples of them. Answers may vary. Check children's drawings.

Additional Facts About Hot-Air Balloons

- Hot-air balloons come in different sizes. The baskets for small hot-air balloons may hold only 1 person. The baskets for larger hot-air balloons may hold 15 people.
- To make the balloon come down, the air inside the balloon is allowed to cool.

Discussion Question

- **Have you ever seen a hot-air balloon floating in the air? If so, describe what you saw.** Answers will vary.

Chapter 11 Geometry and Fraction Concepts

Hot air rises. A balloon filled with hot air will float up into the sky.

Some balloons look as though they have two-dimensional shapes on them. Name some two-dimensional shapes. Then draw some examples of them.

Chapter 11   seven hundred one 701

Intervention Options  RtI Response to Intervention

Use Show What You Know, Lesson Quick Check, and Assessments to diagnose children's intervention levels.

TIER 1
On-Level Intervention

For children who are generally at grade level but need early intervention with the lesson concepts, use:

- Reteach (in the *Chapter Resources*)
- Personal Math Trainer
- Tier 1 Activity online

TIER 2
Strategic Intervention

For children who need small group instruction to review concepts and skills needed for the chapter, use:

- Strategic Intervention Guide
- Personal Math Trainer
- Prerequisite Skills Activities
- Tier 2 Activity online

TIER 3
Intensive Intervention

For children who need one-on-one instruction to build foundational skills for the chapter, use:

- Intensive Intervention Guide
- Personal Math Trainer
- Prerequisite Skills Activities

ENRICHMENT
Independent Activities

For children who successfully complete lessons, use:

Differentiated Centers Kit

- Advanced Learners Activity for every lesson
- Enrich Activity (in the *Chapter Resources*)
- HMH Mega Math

Name _____

Personal Math Trainer
Online Assessment
and Intervention

Equal Parts

Circle the shape that has two equal parts. (1.G.A.3)

1.

2.

Identify Three-Dimensional Shapes

3. Circle each ⬭ . (1.G.A.1)

4. Circle each ⬜ . (1.G.A.1)

Identify Shapes

Circle all the shapes that match the shape name. (1.G.A.1)

5. triangle

6. rectangle

This page checks understanding of important skills needed for success in Chapter 11.

702 seven hundred two

© Houghton Mifflin Harcourt Publishing Company • Image Credits: (tc) ©Photodisc/Getty Images; (tcr) ©Arville/Getty Images; (br) ©Lawrence Manning/Corbis

Assessing Prior Knowledge

Have children complete on their own **Show What You Know.** Tested items are the prerequisite skills of this chapter.

Diagnostic Interview Task

The alternative interview tasks below evaluate children's understanding of each **Show What You Know** skill. The diagnostic chart may be used for intervention on prerequisite skills.

Materials Plane Shapes (circle, square, rectangle), Triangles (see *eTeacher Resources*), objects, sphere and rectangular prism manipulatives

For evaluation checklist see *Chapter Resource Book.*

• Show the child two same-size circles cut out of poster board. Cut one circle into two equal parts. Cut the other circle into two unequal parts. Have the child point to the circle that has two equal parts.

• Place a ball, a rectangular box, and a soup can in front of the child. Show the child the sphere manipulative. Have the child point to the object with that shape. ball Then show the child the rectangular prism manipulative and have the child point to the object with that shape. box

• Show the child cutouts of 2 different triangles, 1 square, and 1 rectangle. Have the child point to each triangle.

✓ Show What You Know • Diagnostic Assessment

Use to determine if children need intervention for the chapter's prerequisite skills.

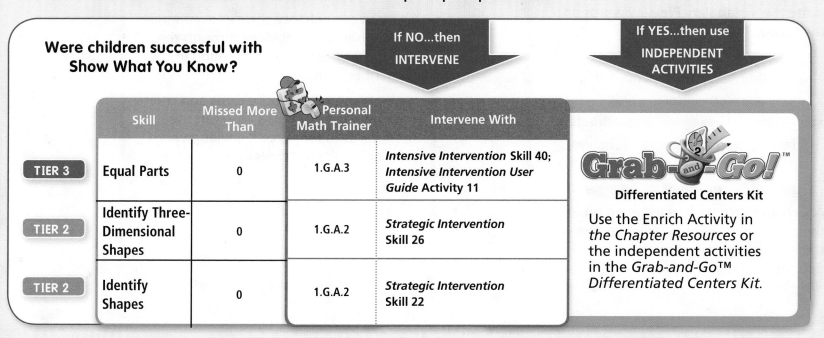

Were children successful with Show What You Know?				
Skill	**Missed More Than**	**Personal Math Trainer**	**Intervene With**	
TIER 3 Equal Parts	0	1.G.A.3	*Intensive Intervention* Skill 40; *Intensive Intervention User Guide* Activity 11	
TIER 2 Identify Three-Dimensional Shapes	0	1.G.A.2	*Strategic Intervention* Skill 26	
TIER 2 Identify Shapes	0	1.G.A.2	*Strategic Intervention* Skill 22	

If NO...then INTERVENE

If YES...then use INDEPENDENT ACTIVITIES

Grab-and-Go!™

Differentiated Centers Kit

Use the Enrich Activity in *the Chapter Resources* or the independent activities in the *Grab-and-Go™ Differentiated Centers Kit.*

Vocabulary Builder  Common Core MATHEMATICAL PRACTICES

Have children complete the activities on this page by working alone or with partners.

► **Visualize It** Have children draw pictures to give examples of equal parts in the green box. Explain that they can be drawings of shapes with equal parts. In the blue box children should draw shapes that do not have equal parts.

► **Understand Vocabulary**

To ensure children understand the Review Word *shape*, point out objects in the classroom that are shaped like a rectangle, such as a sheet of paper.

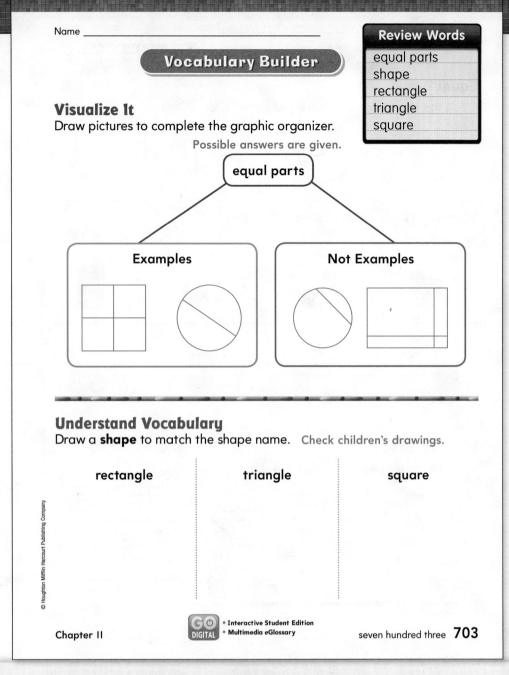

© Houghton Mifflin Harcourt Publishing Company

Vocabulary Preview

Write the Vocabulary Preview words on the board.

cube	sphere	cylinder
cone	rectangular prism	
vertex/vertices		side
pentagon	hexagon	quadrilateral
face	edge	angle	halves
thirds	fourths	half of
third of	fourth of	quarter of

Ask children to define each word on their own using prior knowledge. Use some of the words in context so their definitions can be determined.

Vocabulary Cards

Children can enhance their understanding of **key chapter vocabulary** through the use of the vocabulary cards found in the Student Edition.

Have children cut out the cards and create their own deck of terms. You can use these cards to **reinforce knowledge** and **reading across the content areas**.

Game Count the Sides

Materials • 1 🎲 • 10 🔴 • 10 ⚪

Play with a partner.

1. Toss the 🎲. If you toss a 1 or a 2, toss the 🎲 again.

2. Look for a shape that has the same number of sides as the number you tossed.

3. Put one of your counters on that shape.

4. Take turns. Cover all the shapes. The player with more counters on the board wins.

© Houghton Mifflin Harcourt Publishing Company

Game Count the Sides

▶ Using the Game

Materials 1 number cube, 20 two-color counters

This activity gives children an opportunity to practice counting sides of two-dimensional shapes. In this chapter, the number of sides a shape has is one of the attributes that children use to identify a shape.

Each player has 10 counters and chooses a color—red or yellow. Players take turns tossing the number cube, finding a shape that has that number of sides, and covering the shape with their color counter. If a child tosses a 1 or 2 on the number cube, he or she should toss the cube again. If there is no match uncovered, the child skips his or her turn.

Players take turns until all shapes are covered. The player with more counters on the board wins. If time allows, children may play the game again.

Chapter Resources

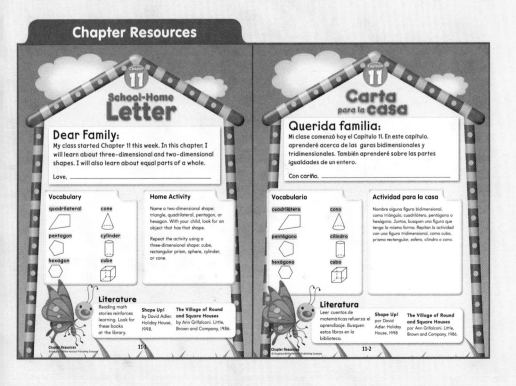

School-Home Letter available in English and Spanish in the *Chapter Resources*. Multiple languages available online at *www.thinkcentral.com*.

The letter provides families with an overview of the math in the chapter, math vocabulary, an activity, and literature to read together.

Geometry and Fraction Concepts   704

Going Places with GO Math Words

Introduce the Words

Provide student-friendly examples and explanations for the words from this chapter, such as the ones below. Then ask volunteers to explain the math vocabulary in their own words.

- An *angle* is formed where two sides of a shape meet.
- A soup can is a *cylinder*.
- Each *face* of a *cube* is a square.
- When you divide something into *fourths*, you make four equal parts.
- A *pentagon* is a shape with five sides.
- A *vertex* is the place where two sides meet.

Math Journal  WRITE Math

Have children draw pictures or use numbers to show what the vocabulary words mean. Then ask them to discuss the words and pictures with a partner.

Going to a Balloon Race:

What You Need
Each group needs:

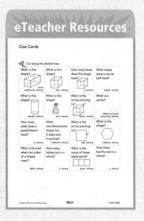

- number cube
- connecting cubes for playing pieces
- one copy of the Clue Cards on *eTeacher Resources* p. **TR221**

Show children

- how to shuffle the cards
- where to place them facedown in a pile.

ELL You may wish to pair beginning English Learners with more proficient partners.

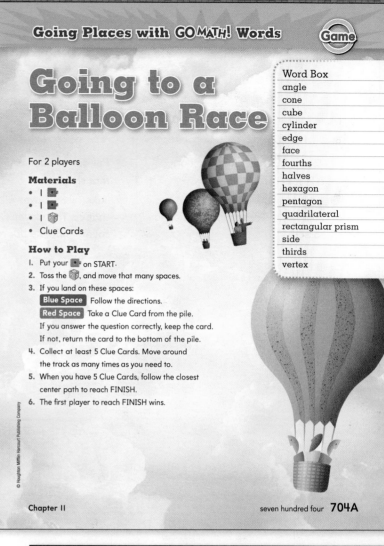

Going to a Balloon Race

For 2 players

Materials
- 1 🎲
- 1 🎲
- 1 🎲
- Clue Cards

Word Box
angle
cone
cube
cylinder
edge
face
fourths
halves
hexagon
pentagon
quadrilateral
rectangular prism
side
thirds
vertex

How to Play
1. Put your 🎲 on START.
2. Toss the 🎲, and move that many spaces.
3. If you land on these spaces:
   Blue Space Follow the directions.
   Red Space Take a Clue Card from the pile.
   If you answer the question correctly, keep the card.
   If not, return the card to the bottom of the pile.
4. Collect at least 5 Clue Cards. Move around the track as many times as you need to.
5. When you have 5 Clue Cards, follow the closest center path to reach FINISH.
6. The first player to reach FINISH wins.

Chapter 11   seven hundred four **704A**

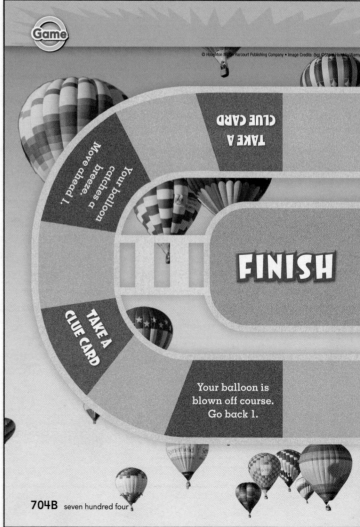

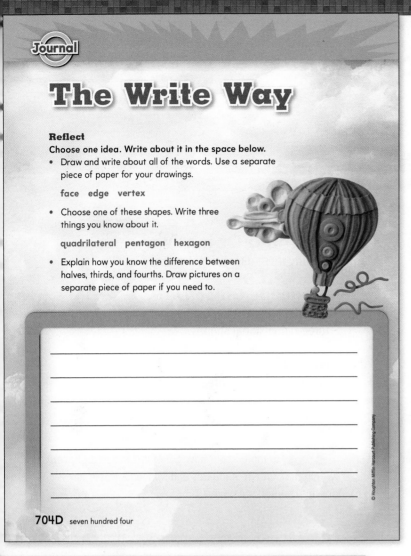

The Write Way

Reflect

Choose one idea. Write about it in the space below.

- Draw and write about all of the words. Use a separate piece of paper for your drawings.

  face   edge   vertex

- Choose one of these shapes. Write three things you know about it.

  quadrilateral   pentagon   hexagon

- Explain how you know the difference between halves, thirds, and fourths. Draw pictures on a separate piece of paper if you need to.

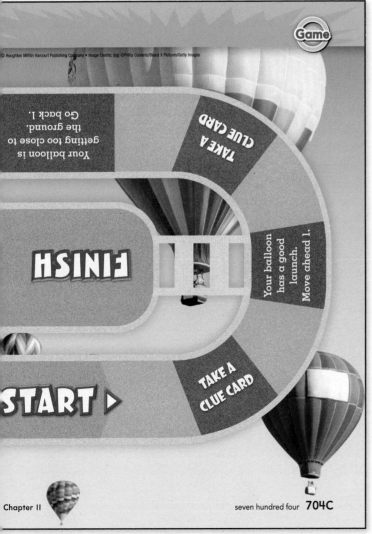

START ▶

FINISH

Your balloon has a good launch. Move ahead 1.

TAKE A CLUE CARD

TAKE A CLUE CARD

Your balloon is getting too close to the ground. Go back 1.

Play the Game

The game may be played before, during, or after the content is taught. Read the game directions with children. Then model how to play the game. Show children how to toss the number cube, read the number rolled, and move a playing piece that many spaces. Demonstrate and explain what to do when a player lands on the different kinds of spaces.

Be sure to explain how a player wins the game and ensure that all children understand how to play.

The directions for playing the game can also be found in the Chapter Resource book.

The Write Way

These short, informal writing activities address the vocabulary and content from this chapter. Communicating about math clarifies and deepens children's understandings about math concepts.

Read the writing prompts with children. Give them time to choose an idea and write about it. When children have completed their writing, ask them to share it and discuss these questions.

- **Does my writing show that I understand the math idea(s)?**
- **Do I use math words correctly?**
- **Is my writing clear and easy to follow?**
- **Do I use complete sentences? Are my grammar, spelling, and punctuation correct?**

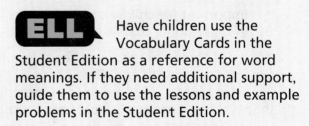 Have children use the Vocabulary Cards in the Student Edition as a reference for word meanings. If they need additional support, guide them to use the lessons and example problems in the Student Edition.

Three-Dimensional Shapes

LESSON AT A GLANCE

F C R Focus:

Common Core State Standards

2.G.A.1 Recognize and draw shapes having specified attributes, such as a given number of angles or a given number of equal faces. Identify triangles, quadrilaterals, pentagons, hexagons, and cubes.

MATHEMATICAL PRACTICES

MP2 Reason abstractly and quantitatively. **MP3** Construct viable arguments and critique the reasoning of others. **MP4** Model with Mathematics. **MP6** Attend to precision.

F C R Coherence:

Standards Across the Grades

Before	Grade 2	After
1.G.A.2	2.G.A.1	3.G.A.1

F C R Rigor:

Level 1: Understand Concepts...................*Share and Show* (✓ Checked Items)
Level 2: Procedural Skills and Fluency.......*On Your Own*
Level 3: Applications................................*Think Smarter and Go Deeper*

Learning Objective
Identify three-dimensional shapes.

Language Objective
Children take turns naming objects that match three-dimensional shapes.

Materials
MathBoard, set of three-dimensional shapes

F C R For more about how *GO Math!* fosters **Coherence** within the Content Standards and Mathematical Progressions for this chapter, see page 701J.

About the Math

Professional Development

Using Three-Dimensional Models

It is important for children to have experiences with actual three-dimensional shapes—not just pictures of them.

If a set of three-dimensional shapes is not available, you can use everyday objects. If you have difficulty finding everyday objects for some of the shapes, you can make the shapes using patterns. Cube, rectangular prism, cone, and cylinder patterns are provided in *eTeacher Resources*.

Provide opportunities for children to describe the shapes using their own words. Have children discuss how two shapes are alike and how they are different.

Ask children to sort the shapes. For example, have them find shapes that can be used to trace a circle and shapes that cannot. Also provide opportunities for children to sort the shapes according to their own rules.

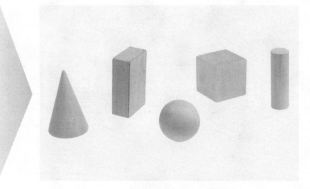

 Professional Development Videos

 **Problem of the Day 11.1**

Number of the Day 15

Show the number 15 in five different ways.
Some possible answers: fifteen; $10 + 5$; $18 - 3$; $5 + 5 + 5$; a quick picture drawing of 1 ten and 5 ones

Have children share their answers with the class.

Vocabulary cube, rectangular prism, sphere, cylinder, cone

> **GO DIGITAL** • Interactive Student Edition
> • Multimedia eGlossary

Fluency Task

Have children review finding the total number of objects in a set of equal groups. Use the combinations below.

- **3 groups of 7**
- **5 groups of 2**
- **6 groups of 3**
- **4 groups of 5**

① ENGAGE

with the Interactive Student Edition

Essential Question
What objects match three-dimensional shapes?

Making Connections
Invite children to tell you what they know about spheres.

What are some examples of balls that have the same shape as a baseball? answers will vary; example: tennis ball **Are there balls that have a different shape than a baseball? What are they?** yes; example: football

Learning Activity
Focus on the similarities that give different objects the same geometric shape.

- **Have you ever seen a brick or an ice cube? What are some other things that have the same shape as a brick and an ice cube?** answers will vary and may include boxes and buildings

- **Have you ever seen a sugar cube? What are some other things that have the same shape as a sugar cube?** answers may vary; example: a die

- **Have you ever seen a roll of paper towels? What are some other things that have the same shape?** answers will vary; any cylinder is a good example

Literacy and Mathematics
View the lesson opener with the children. Then, choose one or more of the following activities.

- Have children decide whether a rocket ship is shaped more like a beach ball, a can of soup, or a cardboard box and explain why.

- Invite children to describe the shape of a roll of paper towels.

2 EXPLORE

Listen and Draw

Direct children to look at the first shape shown on the page.

- **What are some real objects you have seen that have this shape?** Possible answers: cereal box, building block, box of tissues

Have children draw a picture of a real-life object that has this same shape. Children who have difficulty drawing objects may instead write the words or a description for a real object that has this shape. Have volunteers share their answers.

Direct children to look at the second shape shown on the page.

- **What are some real objects you have seen that have this shape?** Possible answers: can of soup, oatmeal container

Have children draw a picture of a real-life object (or write the name of an object) that has this same shape. Have volunteers share their answers.

 MP3 Construct viable arguments and critique the reasoning of others. Use Math Talk to focus on children's understanding of differences in attributes of three-dimensional shapes.

ELL Strategy:
Illustrate Understanding

Draw three-dimensional shapes: rectangular prism, sphere, cylinder, and cone.

- **Write the names of the shapes in a word bank.** Read them and have children repeat.
- **Point to a shape. Point to the corresponding word in the word bank.**
- **Write and say: This is a _____.**
- **In pairs, have children point to a shape and use the sentence frame.**

 2.G.A.1 Recognize and draw shapes having specified attributes, such as a given number of angles or a given number of equal faces. Identify triangles, quadrilaterals, pentagons, hexagons, and cubes.

Name _____

Lesson 11.1

Three-Dimensional Shapes

Essential Question What objects match three-dimensional shapes?

 Geometry–2.G.A.1

MATHEMATICAL PRACTICES
MP3, MP6

Listen and Draw

Draw a picture of an object with the same shape shown.

Check children's drawings.

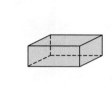

Math Talk: Possible answer: The shapes each have a top and a bottom that match. In the first shape, the top and bottom are rectangles; in the second shape, the top and bottom are circles.

 MATHEMATICAL PRACTICES 3

Apply Describe how the shapes are alike. Describe how they are different.

FOR THE TEACHER • Have children look at the first shape and name some real objects that have this shape, such as a cereal box. Have each child draw a picture of a real-life object that has the same shape. Repeat for the second shape.

Chapter 11

seven hundred five **705**

© Houghton Mifflin Harcourt Publishing Company

Reteach 11.1 ▲ RtI

Enrich 11.1 Differentiated Instruction

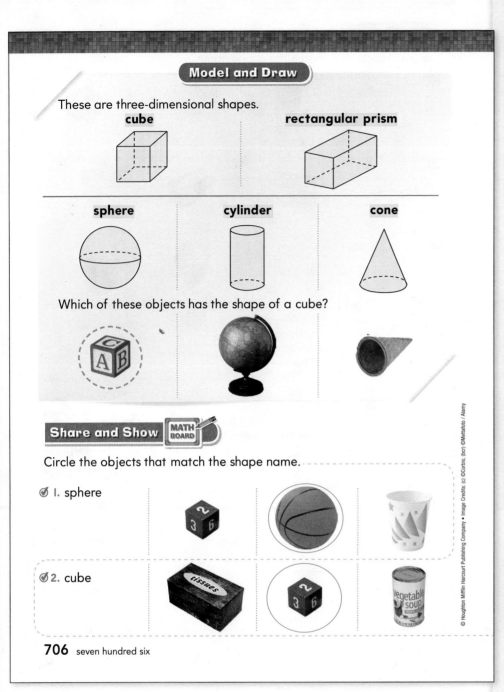

Model and Draw

These are three-dimensional shapes.

cube

rectangular prism

sphere   **cylinder**   **cone**

Which of these objects has the shape of a cube?

Share and Show MATH BOARD

Circle the objects that match the shape name.

1. sphere

2. cube

706 seven hundred six

© Houghton Mifflin Harcourt Publishing Company • Image Credits: (c) ©Corbis; (bcr) ©Mettafoto / Alamy

---

Advanced Learners

Kinesthetic / Logical / Mathematical
Individual / Partners

Materials set of three-dimensional shapes (or objects representing the shapes), clay, index cards, markers

- Display the three-dimensional shapes and ask children to name them. Have children describe an attribute of each shape. **Choose a shape. Tell me something that would help me know which shape you chose.**

- Give partners modeling clay to make different shapes. Have them make labels with the names of their shapes on the labels.

- When children have completed their work, invite them to compare their shapes with those made by other pairs. Have them describe the attributes of each shape.

- Extend the activity by having children find objects in the classroom that match the clay shape they made.

Model and Draw  MATHEMATICAL PRACTICES

Materials set of three-dimensional shapes

MP6 Attend to precision. Some children may be more familiar with the term *solid shape* than with *three-dimensional shape*. Explain that these two terms can both be used for these shapes.

Describe each shape, discussing the appearance of its surfaces. Point out and compare the flat and curved surfaces on the different shapes. Tell children that a cube is a special type of rectangular prism. All the sides of a cube are the same length.

③ EXPLAIN

Share and Show

Connect Exercises 1–2 to the learning model.

- **In Exercise 2, what are the shape names of the objects that are not a cube?**
  rectangular prism and cylinder

Use the checked exercises for **Quick Check**.

Children should use their MathBoard to show their answers to these exercises.

> **✓ Quick Check** ▲ **RtI**
>
> **If** → a child misses the checked exercises
>
> **Then** → **Differentiate Instruction** with
> - Reteach 11.1
> - Personal Math trainer 2.G.A.1
> - RtI Tier 1 Activity (online)

⚠ COMMON ERRORS

Error Children may think that any object with a curved surface is a sphere.

Example For Exercise 1, children circle the paper cup.

Springboard to Learning Have children look at different curved objects that have the shape of a sphere, cone, or cylinder. Talk with them about the differences in the attributes of each shape, to reinforce the different names for these three-dimensional shapes.

4 ELABORATE

On Your Own

If a child answers the checked exercises correctly, assign Exercises 3–7.

THINK SMARTER

Exercise 7 requires children to identify the shapes that have a curved surface and the shapes that do not have a curved surface. Provide manipulative shapes for children who are having difficulty.

 Math on the Spot Video Tutor
Use this video to help children model and solve this type of *Think Smarter* problem.

GO DIGITAL **Math on the Spot** videos are in the Interactive Student Edition and at *www.thinkcentral.com*.

GO DEEPER

Materials various containers that are rectangular prisms, unit cubes

To extend thinking, informally introduce the concept of volume by discussing how much different-sized rectangular prisms hold. Show children real-life containers that are rectangular prisms, such as a cereal box, a crayon box, a tissue box, and a shoe box. Guide a discussion about how the containers are different shapes and sizes. Then have children brainstorm ways they could measure how much each container can hold. Suggest that unit cubes could be used. Have children fill each rectangular prism with unit cubes and count how many cubes fit inside each container.

Name _____

On Your Own

Circle the objects that match the shape name.

3. cylinder

4. rectangular prism

5. cone

6. **GO DEEPER** Julio used cardboard squares as the flat surfaces of a cube. How many squares did he use?

_6_ squares

7. **THINK SMARTER** Circle the shapes that have a curved surface. Draw an X on the shapes that do not have a curved surface.

Problem Solving • Applications   WRITE Math

8. **MATHEMATICAL PRACTICE 6** Make Connections

Reba traced around the bottom of each block. Match each block with the shape Reba drew.

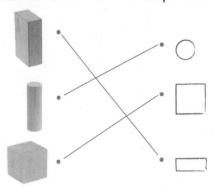

9. THINK SMARTER Match the shapes.

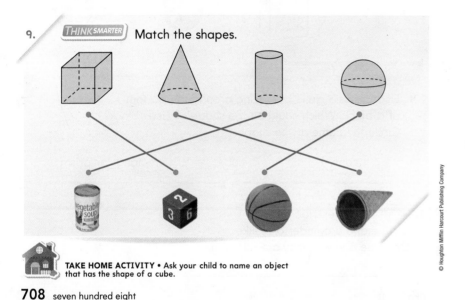

TAKE HOME ACTIVITY • Ask your child to name an object that has the shape of a cube.

708 seven hundred eight

© Houghton Mifflin Harcourt Publishing Company

Problem Solving • Applications

Common Core MATHEMATICAL PRACTICES

MP6 Attend to precision. If some children have difficulty with Exercise 8, you may wish to provide manipulatives for them to use.

THINK SMARTER

Exercise 9 assesses children's ability to connect real-world objects to the three-dimensional shapes they learned in this lesson. Have children explain to you how they knew which objects to match up. Have them identify the faces and curved surfaces of the 3-dimensional sketch and the real-world objects.

5 EVALUATE Formative Assessment

Essential Question

Reflect Using the Language Objective Have children take turns naming objects to answer the essential question.

What objects match three-dimensional shapes? Possible answer: A soccer ball is a sphere. A shoebox is a rectangular prism. A soup can is a cylinder.

Math Journal  WRITE Math

Describe one way that a cube and a cylinder are alike. Describe one way that they are different.

DIFFERENTIATED INSTRUCTION **INDEPENDENT ACTIVITIES**

Grab-and-Go!
Differentiated Centers Kit

Activities
Name That Shape!

Children complete orange Activity Card 12 by identifying three-dimensional shapes.

Activities
Tina's Recycled Castle

Children complete blue Activity Card 12 by identifying three-dimensional shapes and their attributes.

Literature
Building a Mini-Park

Children read the book and learn about three-dimensional shapes.

Practice and Homework

Use the Practice and Homework pages to provide children with more practice of the concepts and skills presented in this lesson. Children master their understanding as they complete practice items and then challenge their critical thinking skills with Problem Solving. Use the Write Math section to determine children's understanding of content for this lesson. Encourage children to use their Math Journals to record their answers.

Name _____

Three-Dimensional Shapes

Practice and Homework
Lesson 11.1

COMMON CORE STANDARD—2.G.A.1
Reason with shapes and their attributes.

Circle the objects that match the shape name.

1. cube

2. cone

3. rectangular prism

Problem Solving (Real World)

4. Lisa draws a circle by tracing around the bottom of a block. Which could be the shape of Lisa's block? Circle the name of the shape.

   (cone)   cube   rectangular prism

5. **WRITE** ▸ Math Describe one way that a cube and a cylinder are alike. Describe one way they are different.

   Check children's work.

© Houghton Mifflin Harcourt Publishing Company

Chapter 11   seven hundred nine **709**

Common Core | PROFESSIONAL DEVELOPMENT | Math Talk in Action

In this classroom activity, children are exploring what the term three-dimensional means.

Teacher:	(Teacher holds up a rectangular prism.) Look at this shape. Who can name this shape?
Matt:	I think it is a rectangular prism.
Teacher:	(Teacher runs a finger along an edge of the prism to indicate its height.) Look at how tall this shape is. This is the height of the shape.
Glenn:	Oh, I see that the height is how tall the shape is from the bottom to the top.

Teacher:	That is right. (Teacher runs a finger along an edge of the rectangular prism to indicate its length.) This is the length. (Teacher runs a finger along an edge of the rectangular prism to indicate its width.) This is the width.
Rachel:	So, the length is how long it is and the width is how wide it is.
Teacher:	Correct.
Kevin:	Does a cube have a height, length, and width?
Teacher:	Yes. Height, length, and width are three things we can measure. Distances that can be measured are called dimensions. Because these shapes have three distances we can measure, we call them three-dimensional shapes.

Lesson Check (2.G.A.1)

1. What is the name of this shape?

cube

2. What is the name of this shape?

cone

Spiral Review (2.MD.A.3, 2.MD.C.7, 2.MD.C.8)

3. The string is about 6 centimeters long. Circle the best estimate for the length of the crayon?

3 centimeters   (9 centimeters)   14 centimeters

4. What is the total value of this group of coins?

16¢

5. What time is shown on this clock?

10 : 30

© Houghton Mifflin Harcourt Publishing Company

FOR MORE PRACTICE
GO TO THE
Personal Math Trainer

Continue concepts and skills practice with Lesson Check. Use Spiral Review to engage children in previously taught concepts and to promote content retention. Common Core standards are correlated to each section.

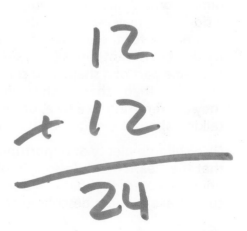

Attributes of Three-Dimensional Shapes

LESSON AT A GLANCE

FOCUS   COHERENCE   RIGOR

F C R Focus:

 Common Core State Standards

2.G.A.1 Recognize and draw shapes having specified attributes, such as a given number of angles or a given number of equal faces. Identify triangles, quadrilaterals, pentagons, hexagons, and cubes.

MATHEMATICAL PRACTICES

MP1 Make sense of problems and persevere in solving them. **MP4** Model with Mathematics. **MP5** Use appropriate tools strategically. **MP6** Attend to precision.

F C R Coherence:

Standards Across the Grades

Before	Grade 2	After
1.G.A.2	2.G.A.1	3.G.A.1

F C R Rigor:

Level 1: Understand Concepts....................*Share and Show* (✓ Checked Items)
Level 2: Procedural Skills and Fluency.......*On Your Own*
Level 3: Applications................................*Think Smarter and Go Deeper*

Learning Objective

Identify and describe three-dimensional shapes according to the number of faces, edges, and vertices.

Language Objective

Children work with a partner to decide how they would describe the faces of a rectangular prism and the faces of a cube.

Materials

MathBoard, straightedge (e.g., ruler), Dot Paper (see *eTeacher Resources*), three-dimensional shapes (cube and rectangular prism)

F C R For more about how *GO Math!* fosters **Coherence** within the Content Standards and Mathematical Progressions for this chapter, see page 701J.

About the Math

Professional Development

If Children Ask

Children may already have words for some parts of three-dimensional shapes. For example, they may call the face a side. They may ask or wonder why they are learning new names for these parts of the shapes. Have children try using different terms (e.g., *side* vs. *face*) to talk about the same part of a shape and see why some words may be clearer than others. If children use the word side when they are referring to a face, others may think they are talking about the edge of a two-dimensional shape.

Give children plenty of opportunities to use the vocabulary that they learn in this lesson. Display various classroom objects that are the shape of a rectangular prism or a cube. Have children describe the attributes of the objects.

 Professional Development Videos

 GO DIGITAL

 **iSE Interactive Student Edition**

 **Personal Math Trainer**

 **Math on the Spot**

iT **iTools: Counters**

 **HMH Mega Math**

Daily Routines

Common Core

 Problem of the Day 11.2

Number of the Day 17
Write an addition problem with a sum of 17.

Have children share their addition problems with the class.

Vocabulary edge, face, vertex, vertices

 • **Interactive Student Edition**
• **Multimedia eGlossary**

Fluency Task

Have children practice drawing arrays of objects. Use these as a guide.

• **4 rows of 3 circles**

• **8 rows of 2 squares**

• **5 rows of 4 X's**

Literature Connection

From the Grab-and-Go™ Differentiated Centers Kit

Children read the book and learn about three-dimensional shapes.

Building a Mini-Park

① ENGAGE

with the Interactive Student Edition

Essential Question
How would you describe the faces of a rectangular prism and the faces of a cube?

Making Connections
Ask children what they know about three-dimensional shapes.

Look around the classroom and find an object that you would describe as a cylinder. Then look for a cube, then a rectangular prism, then a sphere. Accept reasonable answers. **How are a cylinder and a rectangular prism alike? How are they different?** Sample answers: they both have two flat faces and are the same shape from the bottom to the top; one has a curved surface and one has all flat surfaces.

Learning Activity
What is the problem the children are trying to solve? Connect the story to the problem. Ask the following questions.

• **What is the shape of a box of cereal?** rectangular prism

• **What is the shape of a soccer ball?** sphere

• **What is the shape of a can of soup?** cylinder

Literacy and Mathematics
View the lesson opener with the children. Then, choose one or more of the following activities:

• Have children write a story using as many real world three-dimensional shapes as they can.

• Have children write a list of common objects that are in the shape of a cube.

② EXPLORE

Listen and Draw

Have the children read the directions for this activity.

- **The first thing that you need to do is circle the cones. How would you describe the shape of a cone?** Possible answer: A cone has a curved surface. On one end, there is a flat circle, and on the other end there is a point.

- **What is a real object that has the shape of a cone?** Possible answers: party hat, traffic cone, ice cream cone

- **What are you asked to do next on this page?** draw an X on the sphere

- **How can you describe a sphere?** Possible answer: A sphere is round and it can roll.

- **Name some real objects that are spheres.** Possible answers: basketball, globe, orange, soccer ball

 MP1 Make sense of problems and persevere in solving them.
Use **Math Talk** to focus on children's understanding of identifying and describing three-dimensional shapes.

ELL Strategy:
Restate

Children learn the mathematical meaning of the word *face* by actively listening as teachers first use formal terms and then restate them using more child-friendly imagery.

- **Draw a cube and point to the *faces*.**
- **Say: A cube has 6 *faces*.**
- **Have children repeat.**
- **Explain that a *face* is a flat surface of a *three dimensional shape*.**
- **Ask for volunteers to draw smiley faces on each of the *faces*.**
- **Ask: How many *faces* does a cube have?**

 2.G.A.1 Recognize and draw shapes having specified attributes, such as a given number of angles or a given number of equal faces. Identify triangles, quadrilaterals, pentagons, hexagons, and cubes.

Name _____

Attributes of Three-Dimensional Shapes

 Geometry—2.G.A.1

Lesson 11.2

Essential Question How would you describe the faces of a rectangular prism and the faces of a cube?

MATHEMATICAL PRACTICES
MP1, MP5, MP6

Listen and Draw

Circle the cones. Draw an X on the sphere.

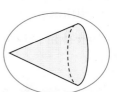

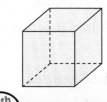

Math Talk: cubes and cylinder; Possible description: A cube has squares on the top and bottom; a cylinder has circles on the top and bottom.

Math Talk MATHEMATICAL PRACTICES

Name the other shapes on this page. **Describe how they are different.**

 HOME CONNECTION • Your child identified the shapes on this page to review some of the different kinds of three-dimensional shapes.

Chapter 11

seven hundred eleven **711**

© Houghton Mifflin Harcourt Publishing Company

Reteach 11.2 ▲RtI

Name _____

Lesson 11.2
Reteach

Attributes of Three-Dimensional Shapes

Two sides meet at an edge.   A vertex is a corner.

A face is a flat side.

6 faces, 12 edges, 8 vertices

Write how many for each.

	faces	edges	vertices
1. cube	6	12	8
2. rectangular prism	6	12	8

Chapter Resources   11-7   Reteach
© Houghton Mifflin Harcourt Publishing Company

Enrich 11.2 **Differentiated Instruction**

Name _____

Lesson 11.2
Enrich

Match Shapes and Faces

Patterns for three-dimensional shapes are called nets. If you fold a net, it makes a three-dimensional shape.

Look at the net. Circle the name of the shape it makes.

1.	(cube) / cylinder / cone
2.	cube / (rectangular prism) / cylinder
3.	cube / (cone) / rectangular prism

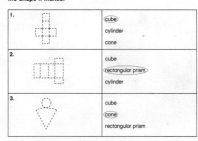 **Writing and Reasoning** In Exercise 1, how did you know which shape the faces on the net made?

Possible answer: I saw that the net has 6 faces that are squares. I know that a cube has 6 faces and that the faces are squares.

Chapter Resources   11-8   Enrich
© Houghton Mifflin Harcourt Publishing Company

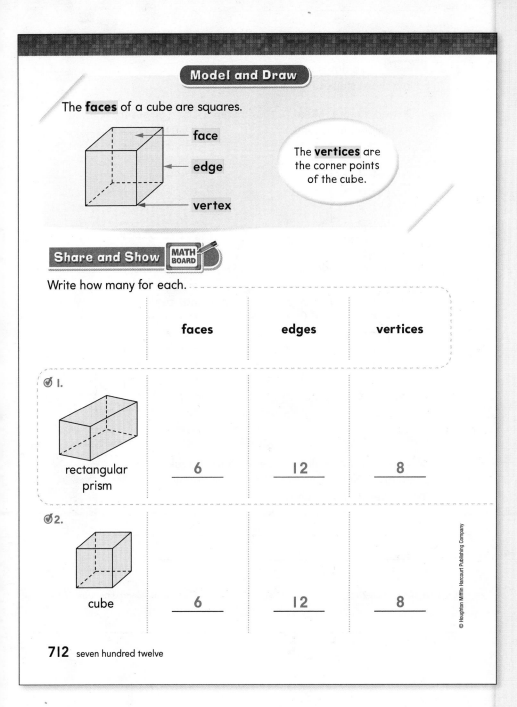

Model and Draw

The **faces** of a cube are squares.

face
edge
vertex

The **vertices** are the corner points of the cube.

Share and Show MATH BOARD

Write how many for each.

	faces	edges	vertices
1. rectangular prism	6	12	8
2. cube	6	12	8

© Houghton Mifflin Harcourt Publishing Company

Advanced Learners
Auditory / Visual Partners

Materials Dot Paper (see *eTeacher Resources*)

• Have one child draw a rectangular prism on dot paper without his or her partner seeing the prism.

• Then he or she describes to the other child how to draw the rectangular prism using the number of faces, edges, and vertices.

• The other child listens to the description, draws the rectangular prism on dot paper, and writes the number of faces, edges, and vertices.

• Have children discuss the differences between the drawings of the three-dimensional shapes.

Model and Draw (Common Core) MATHEMATICAL PRACTICES

MP5 Use appropriate tools strategically.
Work through the model with children. Use the cube or rectangular prism manipulatives (or real objects with these shapes) to explain the meanings of the terms *face*, *edge*, and *vertex*. Also use the manipulatives to demonstrate that not all the edges and vertices can be seen at the same time. These edges and vertices are shown with dashed lines in the picture of the cube.

❸ EXPLAIN

Share and Show MATH BOARD

Connect Exercises 1–2 to the learning model. Remind children the dashed lines also need to be counted as edges, and the place where these lines meet also needs to be counted as a vertex.

• **In Exercise 2, how do you know what parts to count for the vertices?** Possible answer: I count the corner points.

Use the checked exercises for **Quick Check**.

Children should use their MathBoard to show their answers to these exercises.

✓ Quick Check RtI

If	a child misses the checked exercises

Then	Differentiate Instruction with

• Reteach 11.2
• Personal Math trainer 2.G.A.1
• RtI Tier 1 Activity (online)

⚠ COMMON ERRORS

Error Children may overlook some of the edges or vertices when counting, especially those that are dashed.

Example In Exercise 1, children write 9 edges and 7 vertices.

Springboard to Learning Have children make small marks in one color crayon on each edge and in another color crayon on each vertex as they count.

4 ELABORATE

On Your Own

If a child answers the checked exercises correctly, assign Exercises 3–4.

Materials three-dimensional shapes (cube, rectangular prism, cylinder, cone), crayons, construction paper

MP4 Model with mathematics. To extend thinking, have children compare and contrast the three-dimensional shapes. Then have children combine two or more shapes to form a new three-dimensional shape. Ask children to draw the combined shape and describe how they made it to a partner.

To ensure children do not trace the same face twice, you may encourage them to number the sides with stickers or a pencil.

Math on the Spot Video Tutor
Use this video to help children model and solve this type of *Think Smarter* problem.

Math on the Spot videos are in the Interactive Student Edition and at *www.thinkcentral.com*.

Name _____

On Your Own

3. **GO DEEPER** Use dot paper. Follow these steps to draw a cube.

Step 1 Draw a square. Make each side 4 units long.

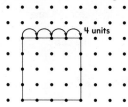

4 units

Step 2 Draw edges from 3 vertices, like this.

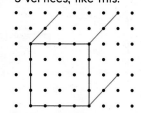

Step 3 Draw 2 more edges.

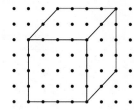

Step 4 Draw 3 dashed edges to show the faces that are not seen.

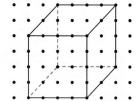

4. **THINK SMARTER** Trace all the faces of a rectangular prism on a sheet of paper. Write to tell about the shapes that you drew.

Possible answer: I drew 4 rectangles and 2 squares.

_____

© Houghton Mifflin Harcourt Publishing Company

Common Core MATHEMATICAL PRACTICES ANALYZE • LOOK FOR STRUCTURE • PRECISION

Problem Solving • Applications   WRITE Math

5. **MATHEMATICAL PRACTICE 6** Make Connections Marcus traced around the faces of a three-dimensional shape. Circle the name of the shape he used.

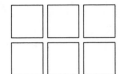

cylinder
(cube)
sphere
cone

6. **THINK SMARTER** Use the words on the tiles to label the parts of the cube.

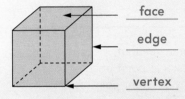
→ face
→ edge
→ vertex

edge   face   vertex

Describe the faces of a cube.

Possible answer: A cube has 6 faces. Each face is a square.

_____

 TAKE HOME ACTIVITY • Have your child tell you about the faces on a cereal box or another kind of box.

© Houghton Mifflin Harcourt Publishing Company

714 seven hundred fourteen

DIFFERENTIATED INSTRUCTION | **INDEPENDENT ACTIVITIES**

Differentiated Centers Kit

Activities
Name That Shape!

Children complete orange Activity Card 12 by identifying three-dimensional shapes.

Activities
Happy Helpers

Children complete purple Activity Card 12 by recognizing three-dimensional shapes.

Literature
Building a Mini-Park

Children read the book and learn about three-dimensional shapes.

Problem Solving • Applications

Common Core MATHEMATICAL PRACTICES

MP6 Attend to precision. For Exercise 5, children must determine what type of solid was traced just by viewing the faces. If children struggle to choose between cube and rectangular prism, show them an example of each to assist them in finding the correct answer.

THINK SMARTER

Children will need to recognize the difference among a rectangular prism's faces, edges, and vertices. Then they will need to be able to count the faces of the prism to determine that there are 6 faces.

5 EVALUATE Formative Assessment

Essential Question

Reflect Using the Language Objective Have children work with a partner to decide and describe the answer to the essential question.

How would you describe the faces of a rectangular prism and the faces of a cube?

Possible answer: All the faces of a rectangular prism are rectangles. All the faces of a cube are squares.

Math Journal  WRITE Math

Describe a cube. Use the words *faces*, *edges*, and *vertices* in your description.

Lesson 11.2 **714**

Practice and Homework

Use the Practice and Homework pages to provide children with more practice of the concepts and skills presented in this lesson. Children master their understanding as they complete practice items and then challenge their critical thinking skills with Problem Solving. Use the Write Math section to determine children's understanding of content for this lesson. Encourage children to use their Math Journals to record their answers.

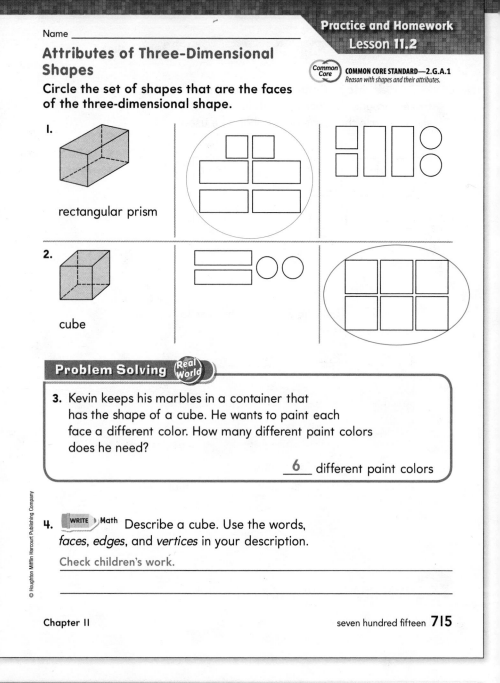

Attributes of Three-Dimensional Shapes

COMMON CORE STANDARD—2.G.A.1
Reason with shapes and their attributes.

Circle the set of shapes that are the faces of the three-dimensional shape.

1. rectangular prism

2. cube

Problem Solving · Real World

3. Kevin keeps his marbles in a container that has the shape of a cube. He wants to paint each face a different color. How many different paint colors does he need?

   ___6___ different paint colors

4. WRITE Math Describe a cube. Use the words, *faces*, *edges*, and *vertices* in your description.

   Check children's work. _____

   _____

© Houghton Mifflin Harcourt Publishing Company

The class is discussing the methods they used to answer Exercise 2.

Teacher: How did you decide which set of shapes matches the faces of the cube in Exercise 2?

Emma: I used a cube and traced each face. I saw that each shape I traced was a square. So, I circled the second set of shapes.

Teacher: Excellent job, Emma. Is there another way to decide which set of shapes matches the faces on the cube?

Dex: Yes. I looked at both sets of shapes. I know the faces of a cube are all the same, so I circled the set of squares.

Teacher: Did anyone use a different method than Emma and Dex?

James: I did. I looked at the cube and saw each face was the same size. So, I looked at both sets of shapes and only the second set had shapes that were all the same size.

Jenn: Well, I counted the 6 faces on the cube and also noticed the faces were all squares. So, I found the set with 6 squares.

Teacher: You have shared different ways to determine that 6 square shapes are the faces on a cube.

Lesson Check (2.G.A.1)

1. How many faces does a cube have?

___6___ faces

2. How many faces does a rectangular prism have?

___6___ faces

Spiral Review (2.MD.C.7, 2.MD.D.9, 2.G.A.1)

3. What time is shown on this clock?

___9___ : ___15___

4. Circle the cone.

5. Use the line plot. How many books are 8 inches long?

___2___ books

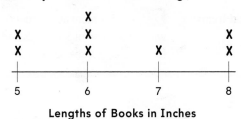

Lengths of Books in Inches

© Houghton Mifflin Harcourt Publishing Company

FOR MORE PRACTICE
GO TO THE
Personal Math Trainer

Continue concepts and skills practice with Lesson Check. Use Spiral Review to engage children in previously taught concepts and to promote content retention. Common Core standards are correlated to each section.

Hands On: Build Three-Dimensional Shapes

LESSON AT A GLANCE

F C R Focus:

Common Core State Standards

2.G.A.1 Recognize and draw shapes having specified attributes, such as a given number of angles or a given number of equal faces. Identify triangles, quadrilaterals, pentagons, hexagons, and cubes.

MATHEMATICAL PRACTICES

MP1 Make sense of problems and persevere in solving them. **MP3** Construct viable arguments and critique the reasoning of others. **MP4** Model with Mathematics. **MP6** Attend to precision. **MP7** Look for and make use of structure.

F C R Coherence:

Standards Across the Grades

Before	Grade 2	After
1.G.A.2	2.G.A.1	3.G.A.1

F C R Rigor:

Level 1: Understand Concepts....................*Share and Show* (✓ Checked Items)
Level 2: Procedural Skills and Fluency.......*On Your Own*
Level 3: Applications................................*Think Smarter and Go Deeper*

Learning Objective

Build three-dimensional shapes using cubes and other objects.

Language Objective

Children discuss and model with cubes how you can build a rectangular prism.

Materials

MathBoard, connecting cubes

F C R For more about how *GO Math!* fosters **Coherence** within the Content Standards and Mathematical Progressions for this chapter, see page 701J.

About the Math

Professional Development

Why Teach This?

In this lesson, children will build a rectangular prism using cubes. They will match given defining attributes of rectangular prisms, such as the total number of cubes, the number of cubes in each layer, and the number of layers. Building with cubes helps children to develop an understanding that rectangular prisms can be measured using equal units.

As children compose a three-dimensional shape, they build an understanding of parts that make up a whole, as well as the properties of the three-dimensional shape. As they build a shape, they identify a shape's geometric attributes and recognize it from different views and orientations. This helps them to develop the foundation for ideas about properties, such as congruence and symmetry.

 Professional Development Videos

 Interactive Student Edition

 Personal Math Trainer

 Math on the Spot

Daily Routines

Common Core

 Problem of the Day 11.3

 Calendar Math How can you draw the boxes of a calendar to show the days of the week? If the first day of June starts on a Sunday, how many rows of boxes do you need?

1 row of 7 boxes, labeled with day names; 5 rows

Vocabulary

 • Interactive Student Edition
• Multimedia eGlossary

Fluency Builder
Repeated Addition

Common Core Fluency Standard 2.OA.B.2

• Display this array of shapes:

Use a hand gesture going across the top row of counters. Remind children that this is called a *row*. Ask: **How many rows are there?** 2 **How many shapes are in each row?** 5 Work together to write the addition sentence to find the total: $5 + 5 = 10$.

• Continue similarly for an array of 3×4 squares. Draw the array on the board. Work with children to find the number of rows, number of shapes in each row, and write the addition sentence to find the total: $4 + 4 + 4 = 12$.

❶ ENGAGE

with the Interactive Student Edition

Essential Question
How can you build a rectangular prism?

Making Connections
Invite children to tell you what they know about building solid figures from blocks.

Have you ever used blocks or bricks to build something? What materials did you use? answers will vary **If you build something that is several layers high, where do you start building?** on the bottom layer

Learning Activity
Focus on what a particular view of a solid object tells about blocks that are not visible.

• **Does it look like the bottom layer has the same number of blocks as the top layer?** yes

• **Could the bottom layer have fewer blocks than the top layer?** no; if a block on the bottom layer was missing, the block that is above it on the top layer would fall

• **Could the bottom layer have more blocks than the top layer?** yes; they could be hidden behind the figure

• **How could you find out if there are hidden blocks on the bottom layer?** look at the solid from a different position – from the side or the top

Literacy and Mathematics
View the lesson opener with the children. Then, choose one or more of the following activities.

• Have each child build a solid figure and draw it from the front and from above.

• Invite children to write about something that they have built with blocks, bricks, or connecting tiles.

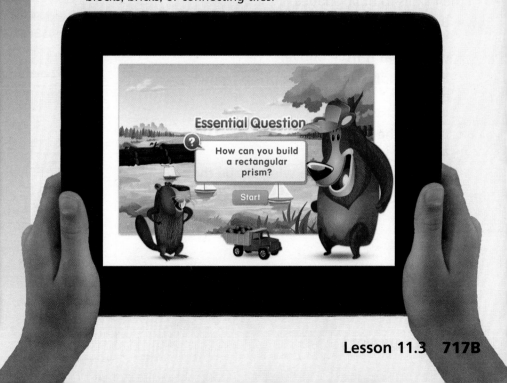

② EXPLORE

Listen and Draw

Direct children's attention to the shapes on the page. Then read aloud the directions:

Circle the shapes with curved surfaces. Draw an X on the shapes with flat surfaces.

Use manipulatives, such as cones or cylinders, to show curved surfaces and flat surfaces.

- **How can you tell which of the shapes have a curved surface?** Possible answers: the shapes that are round or have a face that is a circle have a curved surface; the shapes that look like they can roll

- **How do you know that a face is flat and not curved?** Possible answer: It can lie flat against a table.

 MP3 Construct viable arguments and critique the reasoning of others. Use Math Talk to focus on children's understanding of three-dimensional shapes: their names (cone, cube, rectangular prism, sphere, cylinder), and their specific attributes of curved and flat surfaces. Point to a shape, such as a cube.

- **Give all the reasons why you think this shape has flat (or curved) surfaces.** Possible answer: The cube has flat surfaces only, because every face can lie flat against a table; the sides are straight and there are corners; a cube cannot roll.

Repeat for each shape.

ELL Strategy:
Scaffold Language

Scaffold language to help children develop their skills to build shapes.

- **Build a prism with unit cubes and explain that the *top view* is what we can see when we look at it from above.**

- **Have children look at the prism from above and describe what they see.** Accept all reasonable answers.

- **Repeat the process to explain *front view* and *side view*.**

- **Have children describe what shape they see in the flat surface of each view.** Accept all reasonable answers.

Common Core 2.G.A.1 Recognize and draw shapes having specified attributes, such as a given number of angles or a given number of equal faces. Identify triangles, quadrilaterals, pentagons, hexagons, and cubes.

Name _____

Build Three-Dimensional Shapes

Essential Question How can you build a rectangular prism?

Common Core Geometry—2.G.A.1

MATHEMATICAL PRACTICES
MP1, MP3, MP4, MP7

Listen and Draw

Circle the shapes with curved surfaces. Draw an X on the shapes with flat surfaces.

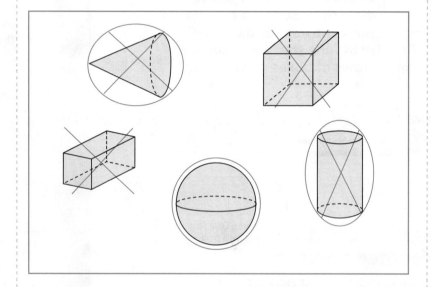

Math Talk: Check children's understanding of the surfaces that different shapes have.

Math Talk MATHEMATICAL PRACTICES 3

Name the shapes you drew an X on. **Describe** how they are different.

🏠 **HOME CONNECTION** • Your child sorted the shapes on this page using the attributes of the shapes.

Chapter 11   seven hundred seventeen **717**

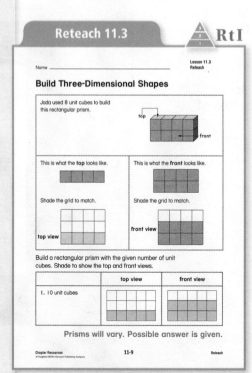

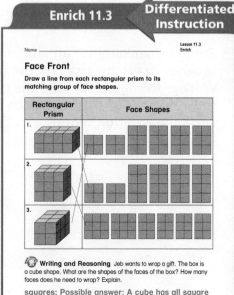

Writing and Reasoning Jeb wants to wrap a gift. The box is a cube shape. What are the shapes of the faces of the box? How many faces does he need to wrap? Explain.

squares; Possible answer: A cube has all square faces. 6 faces, because a cube is a rectangular prism

Model and Draw

Build this rectangular prism using 12 unit cubes.

The shading shows the top and front views.

top view	front view
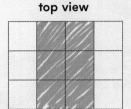	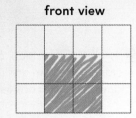

Share and Show

Prisms will vary. Possible answers are given.

Build a rectangular prism with the given number of unit cubes. Shade to show the top and front views.

	top view	front view
1. 9 unit cubes		
2. 16 unit cubes		

© Houghton Mifflin Harcourt Publishing Company

Advanced Learners   Logical/Mathematical Individual/Partners

Materials unit cubes, index cards

- Have each partner draw on an index card the front, back, and side views of a rectangular prism.
- Then have partners trade cards and use the views to build their partner's prism using unit cubes.
- Have them continue as time allows.

Model and Draw Common Core **MATHEMATICAL PRACTICES**

Materials connecting cubes

MP6 Attend to precision. Work through the model together with children, using unit cubes to build the rectangular prism shown. Focus on how the given pictures of the top view and the front view help show the number of cubes in each layer and the number of layers.

- **Look at the top view. How many squares are in each row?** 2 **How many rows are there?** 3 **How can you show this with unit cubes?** 2 cubes in each row and 3 rows

- **Look at the front view. How many layers are there?** 2 **How should your model match this?** Make sure there are 2 layers.

③ EXPLAIN

Share and Show

Connect Exercises 1–2 to the learning model.

- **In Exercise 1, how can make sure your model is a rectangular prism?** Possible answer: There should be 6 faces, 12 edges, and 8 vertices. Each face needs to be a rectangle.

Use the checked exercises for **Quick Check.**

✓ **Quick Check** RtI

If	a child misses the checked exercises
Then	Differentiate Instruction with • Reteach 11.3 • Personal Math Trainer 2.G.A.1 • RtI Tier 1 Activity (online)

⚠ COMMON ERRORS

Error Children may build three-dimensional shapes made up of the correct number of units, but that are not rectangular prisms.

Example In Exercise 1, children make a tower of 4 cubes in one layer, 3 cubes in another layer, and 2 cubes in another layer.

Springboard to Learning Discuss the attributes of a rectangular prism: exactly 6 faces, 12 corners, 8 edges. Have them check that their model matches these attributes.

4 ELABORATE

On Your Own

If a child answers the checked exercises correctly, assign Exercises 3–5. Provide unit cubes for children to use to complete the exercises.

 THINK SMARTER

In Exercise 4, children will need to build the rectangular prism using the views shown, and analyze a side view. You may wish to first show how a side view drawing would look using the rectangular prism that you built together in the Model and Draw.

 Math on the Spot Video Tutor

Use this video to help children model and solve this type of *Think Smarter* problem.

 Math on the Spot videos are in the Interactive Student Edition and at *www.thinkcentral.com*.

In Exercise 5, children will need to shade the side view of the rectangular prism described.

MP1 Make sense of problems and persevere in solving them.

• **Why is the top view and the front view important?** Possible answer: They tell you how the cubes need to be arranged because different rectangular prisms can be made with 18 cubes.

Go DEEPER

To extend their thinking, encourage children to use unit cubes to make all the different rectangular prisms possible that are made up of 18 cubes. They can record by drawing the top view, front view, and side view of each rectangular prism. Possible rectangular prisms include: $l \times w \times h$: $1 \times 18 \times 1$; $18 \times 1 \times 1$; $1 \times 9 \times 2$; $9 \times 1 \times 2$; $3 \times 3 \times 2$; $1 \times 6 \times 3$; $6 \times 1 \times 3$; $2 \times 3 \times 3$; $3 \times 2 \times 3$; $1 \times 3 \times 6$; $3 \times 1 \times 6$; $1 \times 2 \times 9$; $2 \times 1 \times 9$; $1 \times 1 \times 18$

719   Chapter 11

Name _____

On Your Own

Prisms will vary. Possible answers are given.

Build a rectangular prism with the given number of unit cubes. Shade to show the top and front views.

	top view	front view
3. 24 unit cubes		

4. **THINK SMARTER** The top, side, and front views of a rectangular prism are shown. Build the prism. How many unit cubes are used to build the solid?

top view   front view   side view   __30__ unit cubes

5. **MATHEMATICAL PRACTICE ①** Analyze Jen uses 18 unit cubes to build a rectangular prism. The top and front views are shown. Shade to show the side view.

top view   front view   side view

© Houghton Mifflin Harcourt Publishing Company

Problem Solving • Applications Real World   WRITE) Math

Solve. Write or draw to explain.

6. GO DEEPER Tomas built this rectangular prism. How many unit cubes did he use?

_____24_____ unit cubes

7. MATHEMATICAL PRACTICE 7 **Look for Structure**
Theo builds the first layer of a rectangular prism using 4 unit cubes. He adds 3 more layers of 4 unit cubes each. How many unit cubes does he use for the prism?

_____16_____ unit cubes

8. THINK SMARTER + Tyler built this rectangular prism using unit cubes. Then he took it apart and used all of the cubes to build two new prisms. Fill in the bubble next to the two prisms he built.

Personal Math Trainer

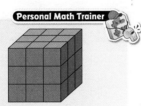

  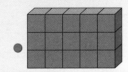

● ○ ●

© Houghton Mifflin Harcourt Publishing Company

 TAKE HOME ACTIVITY • Ask your child to show how he or she solved a problem in the lesson.

720 seven hundred twenty

Problem Solving • Applications Real World

Common Core MATHEMATICAL PRACTICES

In Exercise 6, some cubes are partially visible and some cubes are not visible at all. Children can use visual reasoning to help.

GO DEEPER

You may wish to have children draw a picture of the rectangular prism if the top view was changed to 2 rows with 2 squares in each row.

MP7 Look for and make use of structure.

• **In Exercise 7, how does the number of layers help you find the total number of cubes?** It gives the number of times to add the number of cubes.

 THINK SMARTER +
Personal Math Trainer

Be sure to assign this problem to students in the Personal Math Trainer. It features an animation to help them model and answer the problem. Students first will need to find the number of unit cubes used to build the original rectangular prism. They then will need to find the number of unit cubes used to build each of the prisms shown in the answer choices. Once they know the numbers of cubes, students can select the two prisms with a total number of cubes equal to 27. Students who select either only one or all three answer choices likely misread the question.

5 EVALUATE Formative Assessment

Essential Question

Reflect Using the Language Objective Have children discuss and model to answer the Essential Question.

How can you build a rectangular prism? Use the top view for the number of unit cubes in each row and the number of rows to show. Use the front view for the number of layers.

Math Journal  WRITE) Math

Build a rectangular prism using cubes. Then, draw in your journal the top, side, and bottom views of your prism.

 **DIFFERENTIATED INSTRUCTION**   **INDEPENDENT ACTIVITIES**

 Grab-and-Go!™
Differentiated Centers Kit

Activities
Name That Shape!

Children complete orange Activity Card 12 by identifying three-dimensional shapes.

Literature
Building a Mini-Park

Children read the book and learn about three-dimensional shapes.

Activities
Happy Helpers

Children complete purple Activity Card 12 by recognizing three-dimensional shapes.

Lesson 11.3   720

Practice and Homework

Use the Practice and Homework pages to provide children with more practice of the concepts and skills presented in this lesson. Children master their understanding as they complete practice items and then challenge their critical thinking skills with Problem Solving. Use the Write Math section to determine children's understanding of content for this lesson. Encourage children to use their Math Journals to record their answers.

Name _____

Build Three-Dimensional Shapes

 COMMON CORE STANDARD—2.G.A.1
Reason with shapes and their attributes.

Build a rectangular prism with the given number of unit cubes. Shade to show the top and front views.

Prisms will vary. Possible answer is given.

	top view	front view
I. 12 unit cubes		

Problem Solving · Real World

Solve. Write or draw to explain.

2. Rosie built this rectangular prism. How many unit cubes did she use?

_____8___ unit cubes

3. **WRITE** Math Build a rectangular prism using cubes. Then, draw in your journal the top, side, and bottom views of your prism.

Check children's work.

© Houghton Mifflin Harcourt Publishing Company

Lesson Check (2.G.A.1)

1. Milt builds the first layer of a rectangular prism using 3 unit cubes. He adds 2 more layers of 3 unit cubes each. How many unit cubes are used for the prism?

___9___ unit cubes

2. Thea builds the first layer of a rectangular prism using 4 unit cubes. Raj adds 4 more layers of 4 unit cubes each. How many unit cubes are used for the prism?

___20___ unit cubes

Spiral Review (2.NBT.5, 2.MD.C.7, 2.MD.D.10)

3. Patti's dance class starts at quarter past 4. At what time does her dance class start?

__4__ : __15__

4. Nicole has 56 beads. Charles has 34 beads. How many more beads does Nicole have than Charles?

___22___ more beads

Use the bar graph.

5. Which fruit got the fewest votes?

___apple___

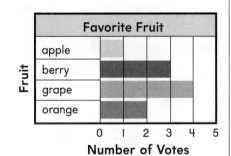

6. How many more votes did grape get than apple?

___3___ more votes

© Houghton Mifflin Harcourt Publishing Company

FOR MORE PRACTICE GO TO THE
Personal Math Trainer

Continue concepts and skills practice with Lesson Check. Use Spiral Review to engage children in previously taught concepts and to promote content retention. Common Core standards are correlated to each section.

Two-Dimensional Shapes

LESSON AT A GLANCE

FOCUS **COHERENCE** **RIGOR**

F C R Focus:

Common Core State Standards

2.G.A.1 Recognize and draw shapes having specified attributes, such as a given number of angles or a given number of equal faces. Identify triangles, quadrilaterals, pentagons, hexagons, and cubes.

MATHEMATICAL PRACTICES

MP3 Construct viable arguments and critique the reasoning of others. **MP4** Model with Mathematics. **MP7** Look for and make use of structure.

F C R Coherence:

Standards Across the Grades

Before	Grade 2	After
1.G.A.2	2.G.A.1	3.G.A.1

F C R Rigor:

Level 1: Understand Concepts...................*Share and Show* (✓ Checked Items)
Level 2: Procedural Skills and Fluency.......*On Your Own*
Level 3: Applications..................................*Think Smarter and Go Deeper*

Learning Objective

Name 3-, 4-, 5-, and 6-sided shapes according to the number of sides and vertices.

Language Objective

Children work in pairs to make a chart that shows the shapes you can name just by knowing the number of sides and vertices.

Materials

MathBoard, rulers

F C R For more about how *GO Math!* fosters **Coherence** within the Content Standards and Mathematical Progressions for this chapter, see page 701J.

About the Math

Professional Development

Teaching for Depth

Children have a variety of experiences with shapes in the real world. Many children may be able to easily identify the names of shapes, but may not understand or be able to verbalize the properties of various shapes.

Encourage children to develop a deeper understanding of the properties that make each shape unique by providing them with opportunities to identify the properties of familiar items. For example, when children are waiting in line with their lunch cards or tickets, ask them to describe the shape of the object by the number of sides and vertices rather than by its name.

 Professional Development Videos

 Interactive Student Edition

 Personal Math Trainer

 Math on the Spot

 Animated Math Models

*i*T *i*Tools: Geometry

 HMH Mega Math

Daily Routines

 Problem of the Day 11.4

Calendar Math What is today's date? If you trace around the box for the date, what shape do you make? If you trace around the edge of the box for the entire month, what shape do you make?

 Have children find similar shapes in the classroom.

Vocabulary side, vertex, vertices, quadrilateral, pentagon, hexagon

GO DIGITAL
- Interactive Student Edition
- Multimedia eGlossary

Vocabulary Builder

Materials *iTools: Geometry*

Sides and Vertices

- Use *iTools* to show children a rectangle. Ask children to name the shape and then check the name of the shape by clicking *Show Name*.

- Click *Sides* to have the sides of the shape highlighted. Guide children to see that all of the sides are straight. Ask: **How many sides does a rectangle have?** 4 sides

- Click *Corners* to highlight the corners, or vertices. Guide children to see that a vertex is the place where two sides meet at a corner. Ask: **How many vertices does a rectangle have?** 4 vertices

- Repeat with other two-dimensional shapes.

① ENGAGE

with the Interactive Student Edition

Essential Question

What shapes can you name just by knowing the number of sides and vertices?

Making Connections

Invite children to tell you what they know about two-dimensional shapes and their parts.

What do you know about rectangles? Possible answer: They have 4 sides and 4 corners.

Learning Activity

Focus on the recognition of different triangles and identification of geometric properties.

- **Draw 3 points (dots) and connect them with straight lines. What shape does this form?** triangle

- **Draw 3 different points (dots) and connect them with straight lines. What shape does this form?** triangle

- **What is different about the two shapes you drew?** answers will vary; possible answer: one triangle is skinnier and pointier

- **If a shape has four sides, will it always have four vertices?** yes

Literacy and Mathematics

Choose one or more of the following activities.

- Have children draw a picture with shapes that have 3 sides or 4 sides.

- Have children make a list of real objects that have 4 sides.

2 EXPLORE

Listen and Draw

Materials rulers

Have each child draw a two-dimensional shape with 3 sides in the first box. Explain that children should use dots at the corners where the sides of the shape meet. They will use their rulers as straight edges for drawing the sides. You may wish to tell children that they will not be using the ruler for measuring.

- **What is the name of the shape you drew?**
  a triangle

In the second box, have each child draw a two-dimensional shape with 4 sides. Children should follow the same process as above, using dots at the corners and their rulers to draw straight sides.

- **Did anyone draw a rectangle?** Check children's answers.

- **Did anyone draw a shape that is not a rectangle or a square?** Check children's answers.

 MP7 Look for and make use of structure. Use **Math Talk** to focus on children's understanding of differences among two-dimensional shapes.

ELL Strategy:
Illustrate Understanding

Draw two-dimensional shapes: triangle, quadrilateral, pentagon, and hexagon.

- **Write the names of the shapes in a word bank. Read them and have children repeat.**
- **Point to a shape. Point to the corresponding word in the word bank.**
- **Write and say: This is a _____. It has _____ sides.**
- **In pairs, have children copy a shape, count the sides, and use the sentence frames.**

 2.G.A.1 Recognize and draw shapes having specified attributes, such as a given number of angles or a given number of equal faces. Identify triangles, quadrilaterals, pentagons, hexagons, and cubes.

Name _____

Two-Dimensional Shapes

Essential Question What shapes can you name just by knowing the number of sides and vertices?

Lesson 11.4

Geometry—2.G.A.1

MATHEMATICAL PRACTICES
MP4, MP7

Listen and Draw Hands On

Use a ruler. Draw a shape with 3 straight sides. Then draw a shape with 4 straight sides. *Check children's work.*

Math Talk: Children's answers may include descriptions of the sizes or shapes of the two-dimensional shapes that were drawn.

FOR THE TEACHER • Have children use rulers as straight edges for drawing the sides of shapes. Have children draw a two-dimensional shape with 3 sides and then a two-dimensional shape with 4 sides.

Math Talk MATHEMATICAL PRACTICES 7
Describe how your shapes are different from the shapes a classmate drew.

Chapter 11

seven hundred twenty-three **723**

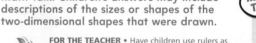

Reteach 11.4 ▲ RtI

Name _____

Lesson 11.4 Reteach

Two-Dimensional Shapes

Count sides and vertices.
A pentagon has 5 sides.   A hexagon has 6 vertices.

pentagon   hexagon

Write the number of sides and the number of vertices.

1. triangle	2. rectangle
_3_ sides _3_ vertices	_4_ sides _4_ vertices
3. quadrilateral	4. pentagon
_4_ sides _4_ vertices	_5_ sides _5_ vertices

Chapter Resources   11-11   Reteach

Enrich 11.4   **Differentiated Instruction**

Name _____

Lesson 11.4 Enrich

Picture Shapes

Use the directions to draw a picture.

1. Use the rectangle below to make a house. Draw a triangle above it for a roof.
2. Draw two hexagons for windows. Draw a quadrilateral for a door.
3. Draw a pentagon for a doghouse next to the house. Draw a quadrilateral for the opening to the doghouse.

Check children's drawings.

Writing and Reasoning How did you know how to draw a quadrilateral?

Possible answer: A quadrilateral has 4 sides and 4 vertices. So, I drew a shape with 4 sides and 4 vertices.

Chapter Resources   11-12   Enrich

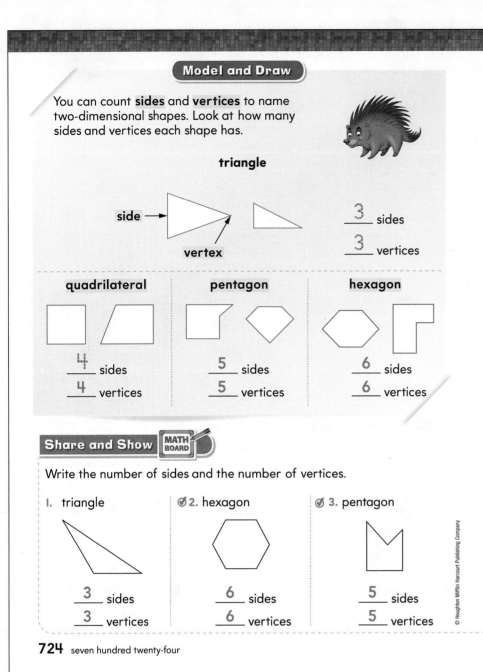

Model and Draw

You can count **sides** and **vertices** to name two-dimensional shapes. Look at how many sides and vertices each shape has.

triangle

side →

vertex

___3___ sides
___3___ vertices

quadrilateral

___4___ sides
___4___ vertices

pentagon

___5___ sides
___5___ vertices

hexagon

___6___ sides
___6___ vertices

Share and Show MATH BOARD

Write the number of sides and the number of vertices.

1. triangle

___3___ sides
___3___ vertices

✓ 2. hexagon

___6___ sides
___6___ vertices

✓ 3. pentagon

___5___ sides
___5___ vertices

724 seven hundred twenty-four

© Houghton Mifflin Harcourt Publishing Company

Model and Draw  MATHEMATICAL PRACTICES

Work through the model with children. After you read each shape name, have children repeat these names. Some children may be more familiar with the term *plane shape* than with *two-dimensional shape*. Explain that these two terms can both be used for these shapes.

Direct children's attention to the sides of the shapes. Discuss how the sides are all straight.

MP4 Model with mathematics.

- **What do you notice about the number of sides and the number of vertices for each shape?** Possible answer: For each shape, the number of sides and the number of vertices are the same.

❸ EXPLAIN

Share and Show

Connect Exercises 1–3 to the learning model.

- **How many vertices does a triangle have?**
  3 vertices

Use the checked exercises for **Quick Check**.

Children should use their MathBoard to show their answers to these exercises.

✓ Quick Check RtI

If a child misses the checked exercises

Then Differentiate Instruction with
- Reteach 11.4
- Personal Math trainer 2.G.A.1
- RtI Tier 1 Activity (online)

⚠ COMMON ERRORS

Error Children may count a side or a vertex more than once.

Example For Exercise 2, children count 7 sides or 7 vertices because they count the same side or the same vertex twice.

Springboard to Learning Have children use a pencil to trace each side of the shape as they count the sides. Have them place a dot on each vertex as they count the vertices.

Advanced Learners 🕐 Logical / Mathematical Partners

Materials index cards, pencils

- Write the following shape names on the board: *triangle, quadrilateral, pentagon, hexagon*.

- Have children work with a partner. Have each child write a list of clues for each shape name on separate index cards. For example, children may write: **I have 4 sides. I have 4 vertices. What am I?**

- Then have children switch cards with their partner and draw and label the shape name on the back of each card. For the example above, children would draw and label a quadrilateral.

- If time permits, have partners draw several different examples for each type of shape.

4 ELABORATE

On Your Own

If a child answers the checked exercises correctly, assign Exercises 4–12.

MP3 Construct viable arguments and critique the reasoning of others.
Exercises 10–12 provide an opportunity for children to solve problems that have more than one correct answer. Encourage children to share and compare their shapes and to tell the number of sides and vertices. Point out that even though the shapes children drew may not be the same, each pentagon has 5 sides and 5 vertices, each quadrilateral has 4 sides and 4 vertices, and each hexagon has 6 sides and 6 vertices.

GO DEEPER

Display the tangram pattern (see *eTeacher Resources*). Identify and discuss that the outline of the pattern is a square. Have children identify the shapes that make up that square. Tell children that the pattern can be cut apart into the smaller shapes. Cut the pattern apart and name each shape again with children. Demonstrate putting the pattern back together again. Distribute copies of a large square and ask children to draw their own small shapes inside the square. Encourage children to include either a pentagon or a hexagon in their own patterns. Have children cut the large shape apart into smaller pieces. Then have them tape the pieces together to make the large square again.

Name _____

On Your Own

Write the number of sides and the number of vertices. Then write the name of the shape.

| pentagon |
| triangle |
| hexagon |
| quadrilateral |

4.

<u>6</u> sides
<u>6</u> vertices
<u>hexagon</u>

5.

<u>4</u> sides
<u>4</u> vertices
<u>quadrilateral</u>

6.

<u>4</u> sides
<u>4</u> vertices
<u>quadrilateral</u>

7.

<u>3</u> sides
<u>3</u> vertices
<u>triangle</u>

8.

<u>5</u> sides
<u>5</u> vertices
<u>pentagon</u>

9.

<u>4</u> sides
<u>4</u> vertices
<u>quadrilateral</u>

GO DEEPER Draw more sides to make the shape.

Possible drawings are shown.

10. pentagon

11. quadrilateral

12. hexagon

© Houghton Mifflin Harcourt Publishing Company

Chapter 11 • Lesson 4   seven hundred twenty-five **725**

Problem Solving • Applications

WRITE) Math

Solve. Draw or write to explain.

13. *THINK SMARTER* Alex draws a hexagon and two pentagons. How many sides does Alex draw altogether?

16 sides

14. *MATHEMATICAL PRACTICE 4* Use Diagrams

Ed draws a shape that has 4 sides. It is not a square. It is not a rectangle. Draw a shape that could be Ed's shape.

Check children's drawings.

15. *THINK SMARTER* Count the sides and vertices of each two-dimensional shape. Draw each shape where it belongs in the chart.

Quadrilateral	Hexagon	Triangle

 TAKE HOME ACTIVITY • Ask your child to draw a shape that is a quadrilateral.

726 seven hundred twenty-six

© Houghton Mifflin Harcourt Publishing Company

DIFFERENTIATED INSTRUCTION   **INDEPENDENT ACTIVITIES**

Grab-and-Go!
Differentiated Centers Kit

Activities **Hexagonal Hopscotch**	**Literature** **Square Fair**	**Games** **Hidden Figures**
Children complete purple Activity Card 10 by recognizing two-dimensional shapes.	Children read about decomposing a two-dimensional shape.	Children practice identifying two-dimensional figures within shapes.

Problem Solving • Applications

MATHEMATICAL PRACTICES

THINK SMARTER

Exercise 13 assesses children's ability to recognize the number of sides in each of three polygons and then add the numbers of sides together. Children may wish to sketch the shapes to count the sides.

 Math on the Spot Video Tutor

 Use this video to help children model and solve this type of *Think Smarter* problem.

GO DIGITAL **Math on the Spot** videos are in the Interactive Student Edition and at *www.thinkcentral.com*.

MP4 Model with mathematics.
Exercise 14 provides children with an opportunity to draw a quadrilateral that is neither a square nor a rectangle. Have children discuss that the number of sides and vertices is the same no matter how they drew the shape.

THINK SMARTER

Exercise 15 requires children to classify each shape by the number of sides and vertices.

5 EVALUATE Formative Assessment

Essential Question

Reflect **Using the Language Objective** Have children work in pairs to make a chart to answer the essential question.

What shapes can you name just by knowing the number of sides and vertices? triangle: 3 sides and 3 vertices; quadrilateral: 4 sides and 4 vertices; pentagon: 5 sides and 5 vertices; hexagon: 6 sides and 6 vertices

Math Journal  WRITE) Math

Draw and label a pentagon and a quadrilateral.

Practice and Homework

Use the Practice and Homework pages to provide children with more practice of the concepts and skills presented in this lesson. Children master their understanding as they complete practice items and then challenge their critical thinking skills with Problem Solving. Use the Write Math section to determine children's understanding of content for this lesson. Encourage children to use their Math Journals to record their answers.

Name _____

Two-Dimensional Shapes

Common Core **COMMON CORE STANDARD—2.G.A.1**
Reason with shapes and their attributes.

Write the number of sides and the number of vertices. Then write the name of the shape.

| pentagon | triangle |
| hexagon | quadrilateral |

1.

__3__ sides

__3__ vertices

triangle

2.

__6__ sides

__6__ vertices

hexagon

3.

__5__ sides

__5__ vertices

pentagon

Problem Solving (Real World)

Solve. Draw or write to explain.

4. Oscar is drawing a picture of a house. He draws a pentagon shape for a window. How many sides does his window have?

__5__ sides

5. WRITE Math Draw and label a pentagon and a quadrilateral.

Check children's work.

© Houghton Mifflin Harcourt Publishing Company

Extend the Math   Activity

Two- and Three-Dimensional Shapes

Investigate Hold up a sheet of paper and a package of paper.

- **How are the shapes of these two objects alike?** Possible answer: I can see a rectangle in each.

- **How are the shapes of these two objects different?** Possible answer: The sheet of paper is flat. The package is not.

Next, hold up just the sheet of paper.

- **What is the shape of this object?** rectangle

Then hold up just the package of paper.

- **What is the shape of this object?** rectangular prism

Math Talk Work as a class to make a list of real-life objects that have the shape of a rectangle and real-life objects that have the shape of a rectangular prism.

Rectangle	Rectangular Prism
postcard	cereal box
top of a desk	math book
baseball card	crayon box

If time permits, have children make a list of objects that have the shape of a circle and objects that have the shape of a sphere.

Summarize Review that shapes that are flat are called two-dimensional shapes. Shapes that are not flat are called three-dimensional shapes. Have children name some two-dimensional shapes and then some three-dimensional shapes.

Lesson Check (2.G.A.1)

1. How many sides does a hexagon have?

__6__ sides

2. How many vertices does a quadrilateral have?

__4__ vertices

Spiral Review (2.MD.A.1, 2.MD.D.10)

3. Use a centimeter ruler. What is the length of the ribbon to the nearest centimeter?

__10__ centimeters

4. Look at the picture graph. How many more children chose apples than oranges?

__2__ more children

Favorite Fruit				
apples	☺	☺	☺	☺
oranges	☺	☺		
grapes	☺	☺	☺	
peaches	☺	☺		

Key: Each ☺ stands for 1 child.

FOR MORE PRACTICE
GO TO THE
Personal Math Trainer

© Houghton Mifflin Harcourt Publishing Company

728 seven hundred twenty-eight

Continue concepts and skills practice with Lesson Check. Use Spiral Review to engage children in previously taught concepts and to promote content retention. Common Core standards are correlated to each section.

Angles in Two-Dimensional Shapes

FOCUS	COHERENCE	RIGOR	**LESSON AT A GLANCE**

F C R Focus:

 Common Core State Standards
2.G.A.1 Recognize and draw shapes having specified attributes, such as a given number of angles or a given number of equal faces. Identify triangles, quadrilaterals, pentagons, hexagons, and cubes.

MATHEMATICAL PRACTICES
MP1 Make sense of problems and persevere in solving them. **MP4** Model with Mathematics.
MP6 Attend to precision. **MP7** Look for and make use of structure.

F C R Coherence:

Standards Across the Grades

Before	Grade 2	After
1.G.A.2	2.G.A.1	3.G.A.1
1.G.A.1		

F C R Rigor:

Level 1: Understand Concepts....................*Share and Show* (✓ Checked Items)
Level 2: Procedural Skills and Fluency.......*On Your Own*
Level 3: Applications.................................*Think Smarter and Go Deeper*

Learning Objective
Identify angles in two-dimensional shapes.

Language Objective
Children work in teams to present how to find and count angles in two-dimensional shapes.

Materials
MathBoard, straightedge (e.g., ruler)

F C R For more about how *GO Math!* fosters **Coherence** within the Content Standards and Mathematical Progressions for this chapter, see page 701J.

About the Math
Professional Development

Why Teach This?
From buildings and bridges to bicycles and buttons, the objects around us are the result of people using geometry. The attributes of different shapes that make up an object often have a specific purpose. For example, the sides and the angles of objects are often a particular length for a reason.

- Explain to children that angles may have a large impact on how things work. For example, the angle of a stair allows for a flat surface on which people can stand.

- Throughout the school day, discuss different objects with children and talk about why a particular shape, length of side, or angle was used.

 Professional Development Videos

 **Interactive Student Edition**

 Personal Math Trainer

 Math on the Spot

 **Problem of the Day 11.5**

Number of the Day 476

Which digit in the number 476 has the greatest value? Explain. the 4; Possible answer: The digit 4 is in the hundreds place, so it has the greatest value.

Be sure children understand that the digit 4 has the greatest value because it is in the greatest place-value position of the number.

Vocabulary angle

 • **Interactive Student Edition**
• **Multimedia eGlossary**

Vocabulary Builder
Angles

Have children draw a triangle and write the name of the shape. Explain that the word *triangle* means "three angles." That is how the shape got its name.

Then have children draw a quadrilateral and write the name of the shape. Ask children how many angles the quadrilateral has. 4 angles

Next, have children draw a hexagon and write the name of the shape. Ask them how many angles the hexagon has. 6 angles

Finally, have children draw a pentagon and write the name of the shape. Ask them how many angles the pentagon has. 5 angles

1 ENGAGE

with the Interactive Student Edition

Essential Question
How do you find and count angles in two-dimensional shapes?

Making Connections
Ask children what they know about sides and vertices of two-dimensional shapes.

Draw a square. How many sides? How many vertices? 4; 4 **Draw a triangle. How many sides? How many vertices?** 3; 3

Learning Activity
What is the problem the children are trying to solve? Connect the story to the problem. Ask the following questions.

- **How many sides and vertices do a pentagon and a hexagon have?** 5, 5; 6, 6

- **How are the numbers of sides and vertices related?** They are the same.

Literacy and Mathematics
View the lesson opener with the children. Then, choose one or more of the following activities:

- Have children write a story that includes as many two-dimensional shapes as possible. Have them draw the shapes to accompany the story.

- Have children identify objects around the classroom that represent triangles, quadrilaterals, pentagons, and hexagons.

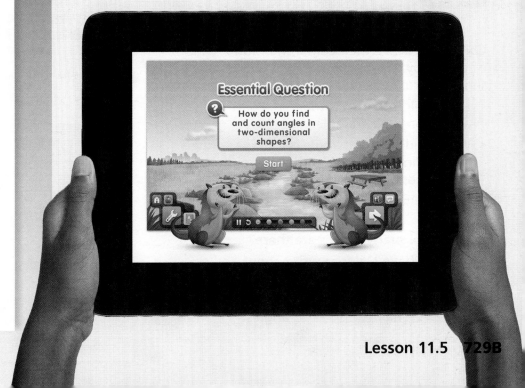

② EXPLORE

Listen and Draw

Materials ruler or other straightedge

Have children read the directions for the activity and then use pencils and rulers (or other straightedges) to draw the shapes. Have them draw two different triangles in the green box.

If children have difficulty using a ruler because of the length, suggest they use another straightedge, such as an index card.

- **How many sides does each of your triangles have?** 3 sides

- **Why can two triangles look different but still be triangles?** Possible answer: Any shape with exactly 3 sides and 3 vertices is a triangle, even if it looks different from another shape with exactly 3 sides and 3 vertices.

Then have children draw two different rectangles in the purple box.

- **How are your rectangles alike?** Possible answer: They each have 4 sides and 4 vertices.

- **How are your rectangles different?** Possible answer: They are different because the lengths of the sides of one rectangle are not the same as the lengths of the sides of the other rectangle.

Math Talk **MP1 Make sense of problems and persevere in solving them.** Use **Math Talk** to focus on children's understanding of describing the attributes of two-dimensional shapes.

ELL Strategy:
Illustrate Understanding

Children practice their comprehension of angles by writing what they see using sentence frames.

- **Have children draw a triangle. Point to the *angles* on their triangles.**

- **Write and read: An *angle* is a shape formed by two lines (segments) that share the same endpoint.**

- **Have children draw a square and circle the angles.**

- **Ask: How many angles are there?** 4

- **In pairs, have children write about angles using this frame:**

  A _____ has _____ angles.
  A _____ has _____ angles.

729   Chapter 11

2.G.A.1 Recognize and draw shapes having specified attributes, such as a given number of angles or a given number of equal faces. Identify triangles, quadrilaterals, pentagons, hexagons, and cubes.

Name _____

Lesson 11.5

Angles in Two-Dimensional Shapes

Essential Question How do you find and count angles in two-dimensional shapes?

Common Core Geometry—2.G.A.1

MATHEMATICAL PRACTICES
MP1, MP4, MP7

Listen and Draw

Use a ruler. Draw two different triangles. Then draw two different rectangles.

Check children's drawings.

Math Talk: Possible answer: A triangle has 3 sides and 3 vertices. A rectangle has 4 sides and 4 vertices.

FOR THE TEACHER • Have children use pencils and rulers (or other straight edges) to draw the shapes. Have them draw two different triangles in the green box and two different rectangles in the purple box.

Math Talk MATHEMATICAL PRACTICES
Describe a triangle and a rectangle. Tell about their sides and vertices.

Chapter 11

seven hundred twenty-nine **729**

Reteach 11.5 ▲ RtI

Name _____

Lesson 11.5
Reteach

Angles in Two-Dimensional Shapes

Two sides meet and form an angle.

There are 4 angles in a square.   angle→

Circle the angles in each shape. Write how many.

1.
_3_ angles

2.
_5_ angles

3.
_4_ angles

Chapter Resources   11-13   Reteach

Enrich 11.5   Differentiated Instruction

Name _____

Lesson 11.5
Enrich

Sides and Angles

Check children's work.

1. Draw a pentagon. Write how many angles.
_5_ angles

2. Draw a triangle. Write how many sides.
_3_ sides

3. Draw a quadrilateral. Write how many angles.
_4_ angles

Writing and Reasoning Look at the shapes you drew. What do you notice about the number of sides and angles for each?

The number of sides and angles for each is the same.

Chapter Resources   11-14   Enrich

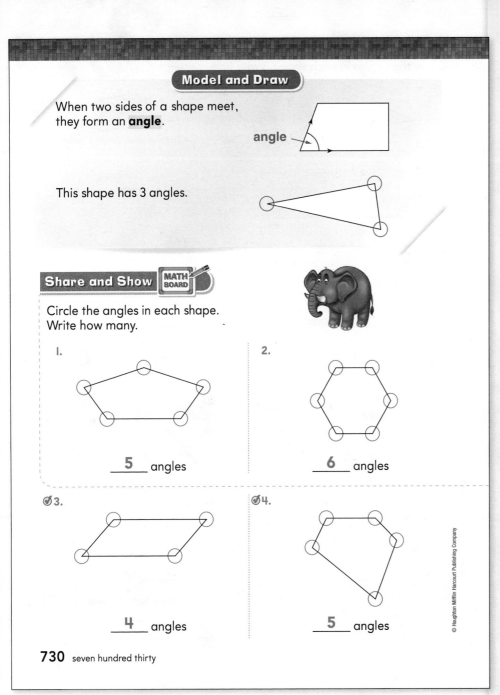

Model and Draw

When two sides of a shape meet, they form an **angle**.

angle

This shape has 3 angles.

Share and Show 〔MATH BOARD〕

Circle the angles in each shape. Write how many.

1.

___5___ angles

2.

___6___ angles

☑3.

___4___ angles

☑4.

___5___ angles

© Houghton Mifflin Harcourt Publishing Company

Advanced Learners Visual / Individual / Partners

Materials Dot Paper (see *eTeacher Resources*)

- Write the following riddle on the board.

  My angles equal the number of wheels on a tricycle. I have the same number of sides and vertices as I do angles. What shape am I? triangle

- Have children draw the answer to the riddle on dot paper.

- Ask children to write a riddle that is similar to the one above about a different two-dimensional shape.

- Have partners switch riddles and draw their answer to the riddle on dot paper.

Model and Draw  MATHEMATICAL PRACTICES

Work through the model with children. Explain that the angles are formed where two sides meet. Be sure children understand how to find and count the angles of a shape.

MP7 Look for and make use of structure.

- **What do you notice about the number of sides, vertices, and angles of the triangle?** Possible answer: The number is the same. The triangle has 3 sides, 3 vertices, and 3 angles.

- **How many angles does the quadrilateral have?** 4 angles

③ EXPLAIN

Share and Show 〔MATH BOARD〕

Connect Exercises 1–4 to the learning model.

- **Before you circle and count the angles in each shape in the exercises, which shape do you think will have the most angles? Why?** Possible answer: I think the shape in Exercise 2 will have the most angles, because it has the most sides.

- **How did you find the angles in the shape in Exercise 2?** Possible answer: I found each place on the hexagon where two sides meet and circled it.

Use the checked exercises for **Quick Check**. Children should use their MathBoard to show their solutions to these exercises.

> ✔ **Quick Check**
>
> **If** a child misses the checked exercises
>
> **Then** Differentiate Instruction with
> - Reteach 11.5
> - Personal Math trainer 2.G.A.1
> - RtI Tier 1 Activity (online)

> ⚠ **COMMON ERRORS**
>
> **Error** Children may count an angle more than once.
>
> **Example** In Exercise 1, children write 6 angles.
>
> **Springboard to Learning** After children have circled each angle, have them write a number next to each circle as they count.

Lesson 11.5 730

On Your Own

MP6 Attend to precision. If a child answers the checked exercises correctly, assign Exercises 5–9.

- **How do the number of vertices in a shape compare to the number of angles?** Possible answer: The number is the same. A shape with 4 vertices also has 4 angles.

 THINK SMARTER

In Exercise 9, children use higher order thinking skills to apply their understanding of the attributes of two-dimensional shapes to complete the drawing of the shapes and count the angles.

 Math on the Spot Video Tutor
Use this video to help children model and solve this type of *Think Smarter* problem.

GO DIGITAL **Math on the Spot** videos are in the Interactive Student Edition and at *www.thinkcentral.com*.

 GO DEEPER

To extend thinking, have children make a chart of the shapes shown in Exercises 5–8. In their charts, children should include the name of the shape, the number of sides it has, the number of vertices it has, and the number of angles it has.

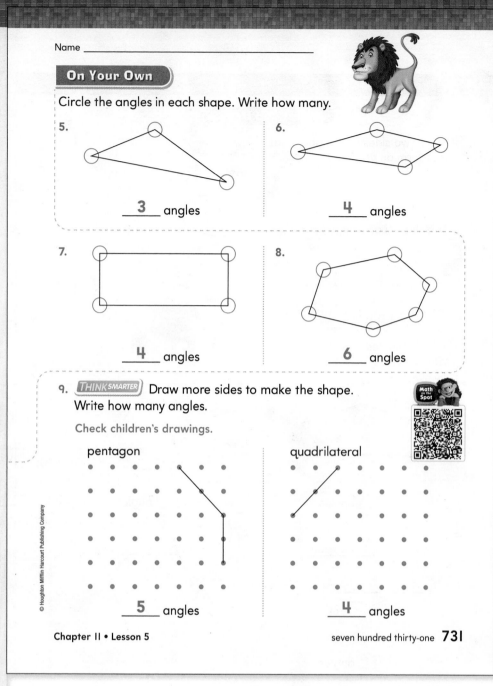

Name _____

On Your Own

Circle the angles in each shape. Write how many.

5.

___3___ angles

6.

___4___ angles

7.

___4___ angles

8.

___6___ angles

9. **THINK SMARTER** Draw more sides to make the shape. Write how many angles.

Check children's drawings.

pentagon

___5___ angles

quadrilateral

___4___ angles

© Houghton Mifflin Harcourt Publishing Company

Problem Solving • Applications Real World   WRITE) Math

10. Draw two shapes that have 7 angles in all.   Check children's work.

11. MATHEMATICAL PRACTICE 4 Use Diagrams Ben drew 3 two-dimensional shapes that had 11 angles in all. Draw shapes Ben could have drawn.   Check children's work.

12. THINK SMARTER Fill in the bubble next to all the shapes that have 5 angles.

TAKE HOME ACTIVITY • Ask your child to draw a shape with 4 sides and 4 angles.

732 seven hundred thirty-two

© Houghton Mifflin Harcourt Publishing Company

Problem Solving • Applications Real World

Common Core MATHEMATICAL PRACTICES

For Exercises 10 and 11, have children use a ruler or other straightedge to draw the shapes.

MP4 Model with mathematics. Exercise 11 requires children to use higher order thinking skills to find a combination of three two-dimensional shapes that have the sum of 11 angles.

THINK SMARTER

This item assesses children's abilities to identify and count angles in two-dimensional shapes. Those who select incorrect answers likely made counting errors, or did not understand the meaning of angle.

5 EVALUATE Formative Assessment

Essential Question

Reflect Using the Language Objective Have children work in teams to present how to answer the essential question.

How do you find and count angles in two-dimensional shapes? Possible answer: First I find where 2 sides meet and circle the angle. I continue until I have circled all the angles. Then I count the circles.

Math Journal WRITE) Math

Draw a two-dimensional shape with 4 angles. Circle the angles. Write the name of the two-dimensional shape you drew.

DIFFERENTIATED INSTRUCTION   INDEPENDENT ACTIVITIES

Differentiated Centers Kit

Activities
Hexagonal Hopscotch

Children complete purple Activity Card 10 by recognizing two-dimensional shapes.

Literature
Square Fair

Children read about decomposing a two-dimensional shape.

Games
Hidden Figures

Children practice identifying two-dimensional figures within shapes.

Practice and Homework

Use the Practice and Homework pages to provide children with more practice of the concepts and skills presented in this lesson. Children master their understanding as they complete practice items and then challenge their critical thinking skills with Problem Solving. Use the Write Math section to determine children's understanding of content for this lesson. Encourage children to use their Math Journals to record their answers.

Angles in Two-Dimensional Shapes

Common Core **COMMON CORE STANDARD—2.G.A.1**
Reason with shapes and their attributes.

Circle the angles in each shape.
Write how many.

1.

<u>4</u> angles

2.

<u>5</u> angles

Problem Solving *Real World* Check children's shapes.

3. Logan drew 2 two-dimensional shapes that had 8 angles in all. Draw shapes Logan could have drawn.

4. **WRITE** Math Draw a two-dimensional shape with 4 angles. Circle the angles. Write the name of the two-dimensional shape you drew.

Check children's work. _____

Chapter 11

seven hundred thirty-three **733**

Cross-Curricular   SCIENCE

Materials pictures of nature that show angles

- Talk with children about where they see angles in nature.
- Have children look in their science books or other resources. Ask them to find pictures of natural objects that have angles. After discussing these objects in nature, have children draw a picture of one of them, showing that its parts have angles.

SOCIAL STUDIES

- Tell children that countries have flags that have different symbols.
- Show children pictures of flags from different countries. Explain that some flags from different countries have different shapes on them.
- Have children point to the shapes and angles they see on each flag.
- You may want to have children name the different shapes on the flags and tell about the number of sides and angles on each shape.

Lesson Check (2.G.A.1)

1. How many angles does this shape have?

5 angles

2. How many angles does this shape have?

3 angles

Spiral Review (2.MD.A.1, 2.MD.D.10)

3. Use an inch ruler. What is the length of the string to the nearest inch?

5 inches

4. Look at the picture graph. How many children chose daisies?

5 children

Favorite Flower					
roses	☺	☺	☺	☺	
tulips	☺	☺	☺		
daisies	☺	☺	☺	☺	☺
lillies	☺	☺			

Key: Each ☺ stands for 1 child.

© Houghton Mifflin Harcourt Publishing Company

FOR MORE PRACTICE
GO TO THE
Personal Math Trainer

Continue concepts and skills practice with Lesson Check. Use Spiral Review to engage children in previously taught concepts and to promote content retention. Common Core standards are correlated to each section.

Sort Two-Dimensional Shapes

LESSON AT A GLANCE

FOCUS COHERENCE RIGOR

F C R Focus:

 Common Core State Standards

2.G.A.1 Recognize and draw shapes having specified attributes, such as a given number of angles or a given number of equal faces. Identify triangles, quadrilaterals, pentagons, hexagons, and cubes.

MATHEMATICAL PRACTICES
MP3 Construct viable arguments and critique the reasoning of others. **MP4** Model with Mathematics. **MP6** Attend to precision.

F C R Coherence:

Standards Across the Grades

Before	Grade 5	After
1.G.A.2	2.G.A.1	3.G.A.1
1.G.A.1		

F C R Rigor:

Level 1: Understand Concepts....................*Share and Show* (✓ Checked Items)
Level 2: Procedural Skills and Fluency.......*On Your Own*
Level 3: Applications...................................*Think Smarter and Go Deeper*

Learning Objective
Sort two-dimensional shapes according to their attributes.

Language Objective
Children demonstrate and explain how you use the number of sides and angles to sort two-dimensional shapes.

Materials
MathBoard, pattern blocks, red, blue, and green crayons

F C R For more about how *GO Math!* fosters **Coherence** within the Content Standards and Mathematical Progressions for this chapter, see page 701J.

About the Math
Professional Development

Using Pattern Blocks

- Pattern blocks can be used to help children analyze two-dimensional shapes. Provide opportunities for children to describe shapes, to tell how two shapes are alike or different, and to sort shapes.

- Pattern blocks also help children visualize how shapes can be composed or decomposed to make different shapes. The blocks are designed so that smaller blocks can be combined to make the shape of a larger block. For example, 6 green triangles can be put together to form the shape of the yellow hexagon.

- Understanding how shapes can be composed and decomposed will help lay the foundation for fractions. The blocks help children see the relationship between a whole and parts, or a whole and equal parts.

 Professional Development Videos

Daily Routines

Common Core

 Problem of the Day 11.6

Number of the Day 75

- **Start with 75. Count by fives to 100.**
  75, 80, 85, 90, 95, 100

- **Start with 75. Count back by ones to 65.**
  75, 74, 73, 72, 71, 70, 69, 68, 67, 66, 65

- **Start with 75. Count back by fives to 50.**
  75, 70, 65, 60, 55, 50

Vocabulary

GO DIGITAL • Interactive Student Edition
• Multimedia eGlossary

Fluency Builder

Ask children to review subtraction facts within 100. Use the ones given below, and continue providing additional facts as time allows.

- **55 − 11 =** 44
- **43 − 19 =** 24
- **60 − 12 =** 48
- **70 − 36 =** 34
- **22 − 7 =** 15

① ENGAGE

with the Interactive Student Edition

Essential Question

How do you use the number of sides and angles to sort two-dimensional shapes?

Making Connections

Ask children what they know about sides and vertices of two-dimensional shapes.

Draw a square. How many angles? 4 **Draw a triangle. How many angles?** 3 **Draw a pentagon. How many angles?** 5 **Draw a hexagon. How many angles?** 6

Learning Activity

What is the problem the children are trying to solve? Connect the story to the problem. Ask the following questions.

- **How many sides and angles do a pentagon and a hexagon have?**
  5, 5; 6, 6

- **How are the angles and vertices related?** Sample answer: a vertex is any corner between two sides; an angle is the space between two sides. There is an angle at every vertex of a shape.

Literacy and Mathematics

View the lesson opener with the children. Then, choose one or more of the following activities:

- Have children write a story that includes as many two-dimensional shapes as possible. Have them draw the shapes to accompany the story.

- Have children identify objects around the classroom that represent triangles, quadrilaterals, pentagons, and hexagons. Then have them identify which shapes have more than 4 angles.

② EXPLORE

Listen and Draw

Materials pattern blocks; red, blue, and green crayons

Point out to children that the same shape appears on the page three times. Tell them that the shape is a special quadrilateral called a *trapezoid*. Have children find a single pattern block that is the same shape and size.

- **What is the color of the single pattern block that you can you use to cover the trapezoid shape inside the first box?** red

Have children color the first trapezoid red. Next, have children find two different color pattern blocks that they can use to cover the trapezoid shape inside the second box.

- **What are the colors of the two pattern blocks that you can you use to cover the trapezoid?** blue and green

Have children use crayons to show how the blue and green blocks can be used to cover the trapezoid. Some children may recognize the blue block as a *rhombus*.

- **What three blocks can you use to cover the trapezoid shape inside the third box?** 3 green triangle blocks

Have children trace the triangle to show how they can be used to cover the trapezoid.

Math Talk **MP6 Attend to precision.**
Use **Math Talk** to focus on children's understanding of ways to sort shapes by different attributes.

ELL **Strategy:**
Illustrate Understanding

Children demonstrate their understanding of attributes by drawing a *hexagon* and presenting their work to a small group.

- **Say: Draw a shape that has 6 sides.**
- **Review that a 6-sided shape is called a** *hexagon.*
- **Say: Circle the angles on your** *hexagon.*
- **Have children color their hexagons.**
- **In small groups have children present their work. They can use this sentence frame, if needed:**

  This is my _____. It has _____ sides. It has _____ angles.

Common Core **2.G.A.1** Recognize and draw shapes having specified attributes, such as a given number of angles or a given number of equal faces. Identify triangles, quadrilaterals, pentagons, hexagons, and cubes.

Name _____ **Lesson 11.6**

Sort Two-Dimensional Shapes

Essential Question How do you use the number of sides and angles to sort two-dimensional shapes?

Common Core Geometry—2.G.A.1

MATHEMATICAL PRACTICES
MP4, MP6

Listen and Draw

Make the shape with pattern blocks. Draw and color the blocks you used.

Use one block.

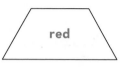
red

Use two blocks.

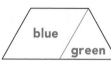
blue / green

Possible answer is shown.

Use three blocks.

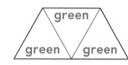
green / green / green

© Houghton Mifflin Harcourt Publishing Company

Math Talk: Possible answer: I could sort by number of sides. The red block and blue block each have 4 sides. The green blocks each have 3 sides.

FOR THE TEACHER • Tell children that the shape shown three times on the page is a trapezoid. Have children use pattern blocks to make the trapezoid three times: with one pattern block, with two pattern blocks, and then with three pattern blocks.

Math Talk MATHEMATICAL PRACTICES 6

Describe how you could sort the blocks you used.

Chapter 11 seven hundred thirty-five **735**

Reteach 11.6 ▲ **RtI**

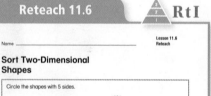

Enrich 11.6 **Differentiated Instruction**

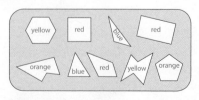

Model and Draw

Which shapes match the rule?

Shapes with more than 3 sides	Shapes with fewer than 5 angles
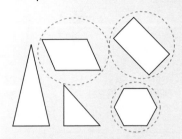	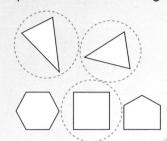

Circle the shapes that match the rule.

1. Shapes with 5 sides

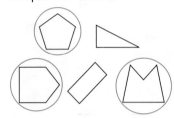

2. Shapes with more than 3 angles

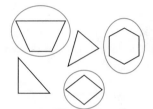

☑ 3. Shapes with fewer than 4 angles

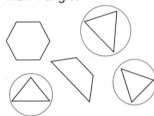

☑ 4. Shapes with fewer than 5 sides

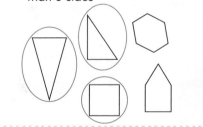

© Houghton Mifflin Harcourt Publishing Company

736 seven hundred thirty-six

Advanced Learners Kinesthetic / Visual Partners

Materials pattern blocks

- Have pairs of children begin with one of each of the six pattern blocks.

- Have one child put the blocks into two groups according to a sorting rule that he or she chooses, for example:

- The other child tries to determine the sorting rule. For the example above, the rule could be: *Shapes that are quadrilaterals* and *Shapes that are not quadrilaterals.*

- Have partners trade roles and repeat the activity using a different sorting rule.

Model and Draw  MATHEMATICAL PRACTICES

MP4 Model with mathematics. Work through the model with children.

- **Look at the first example. The rule is *Shapes with more than 3 sides.* Should you circle the triangles? Explain.** No, the triangles have 3 sides, not *more than* 3 sides.

- **Look at the second example. The rule is *Shapes with fewer than 5 angles.* Which shapes should you circle?** the two triangles and the square **Explain.** The triangles have 3 angles and 3 is less than 5. The square has 4 angles and 4 is less than 5.

Discuss why the two remaining shapes should not be circled.

3 EXPLAIN

Share and Show

Connect Exercises 1–4 to the learning model.

- **For Exercise 2, did you circle the triangles? Explain.** No; Triangles have 3 angles, not more than 3 angles.

Use the checked exercises for **Quick Check**.

Children should use their MathBoard to show their answers to these exercises.

 Quick Check ▲ **RtI**

If a child misses the checked exercises

Then **Differentiate Instruction** with
  - Reteach 11.6
  - Personal Math trainer 2.G.A.1
  - RtI Tier 1 Activity (online)

⚠ COMMON ERRORS

Error Children may misread the rule and not pay attention to the words *more than* and *fewer than.*

Example In Exercise 3, children circle the triangles and the trapezoid.

Springboard to Learning Have children reread the rule and circle the words *more than* and *fewer than.* Have them write the number of angles or sides inside each shape.

4 ELABORATE

On Your Own

If a child answers the checked exercises correctly, assign Exercises 5–9.

 THINK SMARTER

Exercise 9 requires children to use higher order thinking skills to draw shapes based on a given rule. Children's shapes may not all be the same. Invite children to share their shapes. Have children explain how they decided what shapes to draw that do not match the rule.

 Math on the Spot Video Tutor

Use this video to help children model and solve this type of *Think Smarter* problem.

GO DIGITAL **Math on the Spot** videos are in the Interactive Student Edition and at *www.thinkcentral.com*.

GO DEEPER

MP3 Construct viable arguments and critique the reasoning of others. Have children choose one of the groups of shapes pictured in Exercises 5–8. Ask them to write a rule that applies to all of the shapes for the exercise they have chosen. For example, looking at the shapes in Exercise 7 children could write the new rule *Shapes with fewer than 6 angles*, which would include all the shapes. Have volunteers share which group of shapes they chose and the rule they wrote. Ask them to justify how the rule works for all of the shapes that are pictured.

Name _____

On Your Own

Circle the shapes that match the rule.

5. Shapes with 4 sides

6. Shapes with more than 4 angles

7. Shapes with fewer than 4 angles

8. Shapes with fewer than 5 sides

9. **THINK SMARTER** Draw three shapes that match the rule. Circle them. Then draw two shapes that do not match the rule.

Shapes with fewer than 5 angles

Check children's work.

Problem Solving • Applications   WRITE Math

10. MATHEMATICAL PRACTICE 6 **Make Connections**

Sort the shapes.

- Use red to color the shapes with more than 4 sides.
- Use blue to color the shapes with fewer than 5 angles.

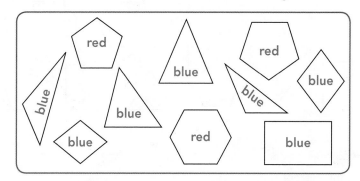

11. THINK SMARTER Draw each shape where it belongs in the chart.

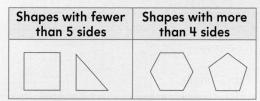

Shapes with fewer than 5 sides	Shapes with more than 4 sides

 TAKE HOME ACTIVITY • Ask your child to draw some shapes that each have 4 angles.

738 seven hundred thirty-eight

© Houghton Mifflin Harcourt Publishing Company

Problem Solving • Applications

Common Core **MATHEMATICAL PRACTICES**

Materials red and blue crayons

MP6 Attend to precision. For Exercise 10, children must identify and color shapes according to the two sorting rules given.

THINK SMARTER

Children will need to be able to sort two-dimensional shapes by their numbers of sides. They first should find the number of sides of each of the given shapes and then draw that shape in the correct column of the table. Children who draw a square in the right column likely did not understand that 4-sided shapes belong in the left column.

5 EVALUATE Formative Assessment

Essential Question

Reflect Using the Language Objective Have children demonstrate and explain to answer the Essential Question.

How do you use the number of sides and angles to sort two-dimensional shapes?

Possible answer: You can count the sides and angles of each shape to sort them and follow a rule.

Math Journal  WRITE Math

Think about the rule *Shapes that have more than 3 angles.* Draw three shapes that match this rule.

DIFFERENTIATED INSTRUCTION   INDEPENDENT ACTIVITIES

Grab-and-Go!
Differentiated Centers Kit

Activities In the Right Direction	**Literature** Square Fair	**Games** Hidden Figures
Children complete blue Activity Card 10 by combining pattern blocks to make an arrow.	Children read about decomposing a two-dimensional shape.	Children practice identifying two-dimensional figures within shapes.

Practice and Homework

Use the Practice and Homework pages to provide children with more practice of the concepts and skills presented in this lesson. Children master their understanding as they complete practice items and then challenge their critical thinking skills with Problem Solving. Use the Write Math section to determine children's understanding of content for this lesson. Encourage children to use their Math Journals to record their answers.

Name _____

Sort Two-Dimensional Shapes

Practice and Homework
Lesson 11.6

COMMON CORE STANDARD—2.G.A.1
Reason with shapes and their attributes.

Circle the shapes that match the rule.

1. Shapes with fewer than 5 sides

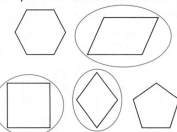

2. Shapes with more than 4 sides

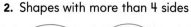
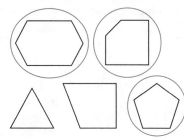

 Problem Solving Real World

Circle the correct shape.

3. Tammy drew a shape with more than 3 angles. It is not a hexagon. Which shape did Tammy draw?

4. WRITE Math Draw three shapes that match the rule.
Shapes with more than 3 angles.

Check children's drawings.

 PROFESSIONAL DEVELOPMENT **Mathematical Practices in Your Classroom**

CC.K–12.MP1 Make sense of problems and persevere in solving them.

As children approach a problem, they should determine what they need to do in order to solve the problem. Rather than rushing to find a solution, children instead need to make sure they have attended to all aspects of the problem.

In this lesson, children sort two-dimensional shapes according to a given rule. In order to sort and classify the shapes, children need to first understand what the attributes of the shapes are. They need to be able to identify the sides and angles of the shapes.

Once children understand a given rule, they need to remember that rule as they analyze each shape in the group. They continue this process for each problem to discern which shapes match the rule and which shapes do not.

Guide children by eliciting possible ways to stay on task and completely work through all aspects of the problems in this lesson. Have several children offer suggestions for the following questions.

Say to children: **Suppose a classmate needs your help.**

- **If your classmate is not sure how to count the angles in the shapes for Exercise 1, what would you tell that classmate to do?** Possible answer: I would tell the classmate to choose one shape at a time and write a number inside the shape at each corner, to show the counting of the angles.

- **Suppose your classmate is not sure if he or she checked all the shapes in Exercise 2 to find all of the shapes that match the rule. What would you tell that classmate to do?** Possible answer: I would tell the classmate to draw an X on the shapes that did not match the rule. Once all of the shapes in the group are either circled or have an X on them, then it would be easier to tell if all shapes have been checked or not.

Lesson Check (2.G.A.1)

I. Which shape has fewer than 4 sides?

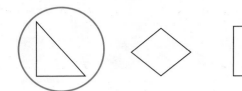

Spiral Review (2.MD.A.1, 2.MD.D.10)

2. Use an inch ruler. What is the length of the pencil to the nearest inch?

<u>6</u> inches

3. Use the tally chart. How many children chose basketball as their favorite sport?

<u>7</u> children

Favorite Sport	
Sport	Tally
soccer	ⅢⅢ
basketball	ⅢⅢ II
football	IIII
baseball	IIII

FOR MORE PRACTICE
GO TO THE
Personal Math Trainer

© Houghton Mifflin Harcourt Publishing Company

740 seven hundred forty

Continue concepts and skills practice with Lesson Check. Use Spiral Review to engage children in previously taught concepts and to promote content retention. Common Core standards are correlated to each section.

Hands On • Partition Rectangles

LESSON AT A GLANCE

FOCUS   COHERENCE   RIGOR

F C R Focus:

 Common Core State Standards

2.G.A.2 Partition a rectangle into rows and columns of same-size squares and count to find the total number of them.

2.OA.C.4 Use addition to find the total number of objects arranged in rectangular arrays with up to 5 rows and up to 5 columns; write an equation to express the total as a sum of equal addends.

MATHEMATICAL PRACTICES

MP3 Construct viable arguments and critique the reasoning of others. **MP5** Use appropriate tools strategically. **MP8** Look for and express regularity in repeated reasoning.

F C R Coherence:

Standards Across the Grades

Before	Grade 2	After
1.G.A.3	2.G.A.2	3.G.A.2

F C R Rigor:

Level 1: Understand Concepts...................*Share and Show* (✓ Checked Items)
Level 2: Procedural Skills and Fluency.......*On Your Own*
Level 3: Applications.................................*Think Smarter and Go Deeper*

Learning Objective

Partition rectangles into equal-size squares and find the total number of these squares.

Language Objective

Children demonstrate to a partner how you find the total number of same-size squares that will cover a rectangle.

Materials

MathBoard, color tiles

F C R For more about how *GO Math!* fosters **Coherence** within the Content Standards and Mathematical Progressions for this chapter, see page 701J.

About the Math

Professional Development

Why Teach This?

In this lesson, children use square color tiles to cover a rectangle. Then they trace around the square color tiles. Using the square color tiles as a concrete tool to partition rectangles helps children build a foundation for determining the area of rectangles in later grades.

After children partition the rectangles with the square color tiles, they identify how many rows and columns they have divided the rectangle into and then write the total number of square tiles they used to cover the rectangle. Using color tiles, model how to partition a rectangle into two rows and three columns. Point out for children what a row is and what a column is. Then demonstrate how to find the total number of square tiles used to cover the rectangle.

 Professional Development Videos

 GO DIGITAL

 **SE Interactive Student Edition**

 **Personal Math Trainer**

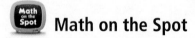 **Math on the Spot**

Daily Routines
Common Core

 Problem of the Day 11.7

Words of the
Day minute hour a.m. p.m.
noon midnight

Choose one word or abbreviation. Use the word or abbreviation in a sentence.

Have children share their sentences with the class.

Vocabulary

 • Interactive Student Edition
• Multimedia eGlossary

Fluency Builder
Basic Facts

> **Common Core Fluency**
> **Standard** 2.0A.B.2

Add or subtract.

1. $8 + 6 = \underline{14}$

2. $5 + 7 = \underline{12}$

3. $6 - 2 = \underline{4}$

4. $10 + 9 = \underline{19}$

5. $14 - 8 = \underline{6}$

6. $20 - 10 = \underline{10}$

7. $7 + 4 = \underline{11}$

① ENGAGE

with the Interactive Student Edition

Essential Question
How do you find the total number of same-size squares that will cover a rectangle?

Making Connections
Invite children to tell you what they know about measuring area.

Have you ever tried to compare two rooms to decide which one is bigger? How could you decide by measuring with a measuring tape? if one room is longer and also wider, it would be bigger **If one of the rooms is longer, but the other is wider, how could you decide?** answers will vary; sample: find some way to see which room has a bigger floor

Learning Activity
Focus on the idea that there is only one answer when a surface is measured by covering it with square tiles that are the same size.

• **How can you place squares on top of a surface so that they completely cover it?** make a row of squares, then another row until the surface is covered

• **If someone else covered the surface with the same square tiles, do you think they would get a different answer or the same answer? Why?** same answer because there is only one way to cover the surface

Literacy and Mathematics
View the lesson opener with the children. Then, choose one or more of the following activities.

• Have children use square tiles to find two different rectangles that it takes 6 tiles to cover. Have them draw the outline around both figures.

• Have children write a story about two rectangles that argued about who was bigger.

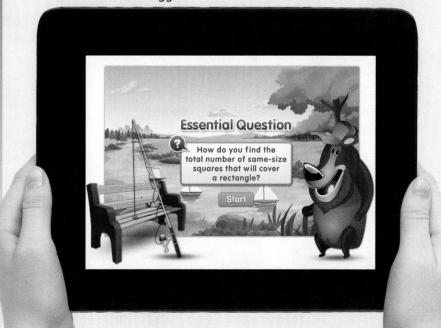

2 EXPLORE

Listen and Draw

Materials color tiles

Have children read the directions for the activity. Then have them put several color tiles together and trace around their shape to draw a two-dimensional shape. If children have difficulty keeping the tiles from moving while tracing, you may want to have children work in pairs. One child holds the tiles in place while the other child traces around them.

- **Can you make a square with the same number of color tiles? Explain.** Answers will vary depending on how many color tiles children used.

- **How many sides does your two-dimensional shape have?** Answers will vary depending on the way children arranged the tiles.

Depending on the tile arrangements used, children may not be able to name the two-dimensional shape they have drawn. Check that they can identify the number of sides that it has.

 MP3 Construct viable arguments and critique the reasoning of others. Use **Math Talk** to focus on children's understanding of different ways to arrange square color tiles to make different shapes.

 Strategy:

Scaffold Language

Display the words *square tiles, rows, columns,* and *total* in a word bank.

- **Point and read the words, then have children repeat.**

- **Review what the words mean.**

- **Draw a rectangle that is partitioned into 4 rows and 2 columns on the board.**

- **In small groups, have the children use the words from the word bank to discuss and write about the rectangle.**

Common Core 2.G.A.2 Partition a rectangle into rows and columns of same-size squares and count to find the total number of them.
2.OA.C.4 Use addition to find the total number of objects arranged in rectangular arrays with up to 5 rows and up to 5 columns; write an equation to express the total as a sum of equal addends.

Name _____

HANDS ON
Lesson 11.7

Partition Rectangles

Essential Question How do you find the total number of same-size squares that will cover a rectangle?

Common Core Geometry—2.G.A.2
Also 2.OA.C.4
MATHEMATICAL PRACTICES
MP3, MP5, MP8

Listen and Draw

Put several color tiles together. Trace around the shape to draw a two-dimensional shape.

Check children's work.

Math Talk: Yes; Possible explanation: The tiles could be arranged in a different way to make a shorter, wider shape.

Math Talk MATHEMATICAL PRACTICES 3

Is there a different shape that can be made with the same number of tiles? **Explain.**

HOME CONNECTION • After putting together tiles, your child traced around them to draw a two-dimensional shape. This activity is an introduction to partitioning a rectangle into several same-size squares.

Chapter 11

seven hundred forty-one **741**

Reteach 11.7 ▲ **RtI**

Name _____

Lesson 11.7
Reteach

Partition Rectangles

How many square tiles cover this rectangle?

Make a row of color tiles on the rectangle. Trace around the square tiles.

_3_ square tiles

Use color tiles to cover the rectangle. Trace around the square tiles. Write how many.

1.

2.

Number of rows: _2_
Number of columns: _2_
Total: _4_ square tiles

Number of rows: _3_
Number of columns: _1_
Total: _3_ square tiles

Chapter Resources
© Houghton Mifflin Harcourt Publishing Company

11-17

Reteach

Enrich 11.7

Differentiated Instruction

Name _____

Lesson 11.7
Enrich

Guess and Check

Children's guesses may vary.

Guess how many square tiles you would need to cover the rectangle. Write your guess. Then cover the rectangle with color tiles and write the number.

1.

My guess: _____ square tiles
Number needed: _4_ square tiles

2.

My guess: _____ square tiles
Number needed: _6_ square tiles

Writing and Reasoning How did you decide how many square tiles to guess for the second rectangle?

Possible answer: I looked to see how many tiles might fit in each row. Then I looked to see if more than one row of tiles would fit.

Chapter Resources
© Houghton Mifflin Harcourt Publishing Company

11-18

Enrich

Model and Draw

Trace around color tiles. How many square tiles cover this rectangle?

Number of rows: __2__

Number of columns: __3__

Total: __6__ square tiles

© Houghton Mifflin Harcourt Publishing Company

Share and Show MATH BOARD

Use color tiles to cover the rectangle.
Trace around the square tiles. Write how many.

✓ 1.

Number of rows: __2__

Number of columns: __2__

Total: __4__ square tiles

✓ 2.

Number of rows: __1__

Number of columns: __3__

Total: __3__ square tiles

Model and Draw  MATHEMATICAL PRACTICES

Work through the model with children. Remind children that rows go from side to side and columns go up and down.

- **How are the tiles arranged?** Possible answer: The tiles are lined up side by side and do not overlap.

MP8 Look for and express regularity in repeated reasoning.

- **Can you use 8 tiles to cover the rectangle? Explain.** No. Possible answer: Six tiles cover the rectangle exactly. Two more tiles would go outside of the rectangle outline.

③ EXPLAIN

Share and Show MATH BOARD

Connect Exercises 1–2 to the learning model. Guide children in lining up the tiles with the sides of the rectangles and then tracing around the tiles.

- **In Exercise 1, how many square tiles are used to cover the rectangle?** 4 square tiles

Use the checked exercises for Quick Check. Children should use their MathBoard to show their solutions to these exercises.

✓ Quick Check RtI

If → a child misses the checked exercises

Then → Differentiate Instruction with
- Reteach 11.7
- Personal Math trainer 2.G.A.2, 2.OA.C.4
- RtI Tier 1 Activity (online)

⚠ COMMON ERRORS

Error Children may trace two tiles and notice the last square does not need to be traced and then miscount the squares.

Example In Exercise 2, children write 2 for the total square tiles.

Springboard to Learning Remind children to cover the rectangle with tiles first and then trace the tiles. Have children number the squares as they count them.

Lesson 11.7   742

4 ELABORATE

On Your Own

If a child answers the checked exercises correctly, assign Exercises 3–5.

 THINK SMARTER

MP5 Use appropriate tools strategically.
In Exercise 5, children use higher order thinking skills to estimate the number of ones blocks that will fit on the rectangle without using concrete materials.

 Math on the Spot Video Tutor
Use this video to help children model and solve this type of *Think Smarter* problem.

 Math on the Spot videos are in the Interactive Student Edition and at *www.thinkcentral.com*.

5 EVALUATE — Formative Assessment

Essential Question

Reflect Using the Language Objective Have children answer the essential question by demonstrating to a partner.

How do you find the total number of same size squares that will cover a rectangle?

Possible answer: First, I use tiles to cover the rectangle. Then I trace each tile on the rectangle and count the number of tiles I used.

Math Journal

 **WRITE Math**

Look at Exercise 3 on page 743. Is there a different-shaped rectangle that you could cover with 6 tiles? Explain.

Name _____

 **On Your Own**

Use color tiles to cover the rectangle.
Trace around the square tiles. Write how many.

3.

Number of rows: __2__

Number of columns: __3__

Total: __6__ square tiles

4.

Number of rows: __1__

Number of columns: __2__

Total: __2__ square tiles

5. **THINK SMARTER** Mary started to cover this rectangle with ones blocks. **Explain** how you would estimate the number of ones blocks that would cover the whole rectangle.

Possible answer: I estimate that there

would be 2 more rows of 3 squares,

so that would be 6 rows of 3 squares: 18 ones blocks in all.

© Houghton Mifflin Harcourt Publishing Company

 **TAKE HOME ACTIVITY** • Have your child describe what he or she did in this lesson.

DIFFERENTIATED INSTRUCTION | **INDEPENDENT ACTIVITIES**

Grab-and-Go!

Differentiated Centers Kit

Activities *Pieced Together*	*Literature* *Taking Shape*	*Games* *Hidden Figures*
Children complete orange Activity Card 10 by combining pattern blocks to make polygons.	Children read about combining shapes within other shapes.	Children practice identifying two-dimensional figures within shapes.

Name _____

Concepts and Skills

Circle the objects that match the shape name. (2.G.A.1)

1. cylinder				
2. cube				

Write the number of sides and the number of vertices. (2.G.A.1)

3. quadrilateral

__4__ sides

__4__ vertices

4. pentagon

__5__ sides

__5__ vertices

5. hexagon

__6__ sides

__6__ vertices

6. *THINK SMARTER* How many angles does this shape have? (2.G.A.1)

__5__ angles

744 seven hundred forty-four

Formative Assessment

Use the **Mid-Chapter Checkpoint** to assess children's learning and progress in the first half of the chapter. The formative assessment provides the opportunity to adjust teaching methods for individual or whole class instruction.

THINK SMARTER

This exercise assesses children's ability to locate and count angles on a shape. Have children circle each angle as they count it.

✓ Data-Driven Decision Making 🔺 RtI

Based on the results of the Mid-Chapter Checkpoint, use the following resources to strengthen individual or whole class instruction.

Item	Lesson	Standards	Common Error	Personal Math Trainer	Intervene with
1	11.1	2.G.A.1	May think that any object with a curved surface is a cylinder	2.G.A.1	R—11.1
2	11.1	2.G.A.1	May think that any object with a flat surface is a cube	2.G.A.1	R—11.1
3–5	11.4	2.G.A.1	May miscount number of sides and vertices	2.G.A.1	R—11.4
6	11.5	2.G.A.1	May count an angle more than once	2.G.A.1	R—11.5

Key: R—Reteach (in the *Chapter Resources*)

Practice and Homework

Use the Practice and Homework pages to provide children with more practice of the concepts and skills presented in this lesson. Children master their understanding as they complete practice items and then challenge their critical thinking skills with Problem Solving. Use the Write Math section to determine children's understanding of content for this lesson. Encourage children to use their Math Journals to record their answers.

Partition Rectangles

Use color tiles to cover the rectangle.
Trace around the square tiles.
Write how many.

Common Core **COMMON CORE STANDARD—2.G.A.2**
Reason with shapes and their attributes.

1.

Number of rows: __2__

Number of columns: __3__

Total: __6__ square tiles

2.

Number of rows: __1__

Number of columns: __2__

Total: __2__ square tiles

Problem Solving (Real World)

Solve. Write or draw to explain.

3. Nina wants to put color tiles on a square. 3 color tiles fit across the top of the square. How many rows and columns of tiles will Nina need? How many square tiles will she use in all?

Number of rows: __3__

Number of columns: __3__

Total: __9__ square tiles

4. **WRITE** Math Look at Exercise 1 above. Is there a different rectangle that you could cover with 6 color tiles? Explain.

Check children's work.
_____

© Houghton Mifflin Harcourt Publishing Company

Chapter 11

seven hundred forty-five **745**

Lesson Check (2.G.A.2)

I. Gina uses color tiles to cover the rectangle. How many square tiles does she use?

<u>3</u> square tiles

Spiral Review (2.MD.D.10, 2.G.A.1)

2. How many faces does a cube have?

<u>6</u> faces

3. How many angles does this shape have?

<u>6</u> angles

4. Use the tally chart. How many more children chose art than reading?

<u>2</u> more children

Favorite Subject	
Subject	Tally
reading	卌 ⫿⫿⫿
math	卌 ⫿⫿⫿⫿
science	卌
art	卌 卌

© Houghton Mifflin Harcourt Publishing Company

FOR MORE PRACTICE
GO TO THE
Personal Math Trainer

Continue concepts and skills practice with Lesson Check. Use Spiral Review to engage children in previously taught concepts and to promote content retention. Common Core standards are correlated to each section.

Equal Parts

LESSON AT A GLANCE

FOCUS **COHERENCE** **RIGOR**

F C R Focus:

 Common Core State Standards

2.G.A.3 Partition circles and rectangles into two, three, or four equal shares, describe the shares using the words *halves, thirds, half of, a third of*, etc., and describe the whole as two halves, three thirds, four fourths. Recognize that equal shares of identical wholes need not have the same shape.

MATHEMATICAL PRACTICES
MP1 Make sense of problems and persevere in solving them. **MP3** Construct viable arguments and critique the reasoning of others. **MP6** Attend to precision. **MP8** Look for and express regularity in repeated reasoning.

F C R Coherence:

Standards Across the Grades
Before	Grade 2	After
1.G.A.3	2.G.A.3	3.G.A.2

F C R Rigor:

Level 1: Understand Concepts.................*Share and Show* (✓ Checked Items)
Level 2: Procedural Skills and Fluency.......*On Your Own*
Level 3: Applications................................*Think Smarter and Go Deeper*

Learning Objective
Identify and name equal parts of circles and rectangles as halves, thirds, or fourths.

Language Objective
Children draw examples on their MathBoard of halves, thirds, and fourths of a whole.

Materials
MathBoard, pattern blocks, red and blue crayons

F C R For more about how *GO Math!* fosters **Coherence** within the Content Standards and Mathematical Progressions for this chapter, see page 701J..

About the Math
Professional Development

If Children Ask

Children may wonder why they are learning to find equal parts of a whole. They are probably familiar with equal parts from situations such as the following.

- splitting the last piece of dessert into equal parts

- cutting a sandwich into equal parts

- sharing a pizza equally with friends

Discuss these examples. Then have children give other examples of how equal parts are used in their lives. Connect the concept of equal parts to measurement. Display an inch ruler and discuss the 12 inches as equal parts of one foot.

 Professional Development Videos

 GO DIGITAL

 **SE** Interactive Student Edition

 Personal Math Trainer

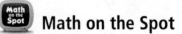 Math on the Spot

 **MM** HMH Mega Math

Daily Routines
Common Core

 **Problem of the Day 11.8**

Word of the Day equal

Complete the following sentences.

10 plus 10 is equal to __20__.

43 plus 4 is equal to __47__.

100 plus 62 is equal to __162__.

Have children complete the sentences and read them aloud.

Vocabulary **halves, thirds, fourths**

GO DIGITAL
• Interactive Student Edition
• Multimedia eGlossary

Vocabulary Builder

Materials paper plates

Halves, Thirds, and Fourths

• Show children a paper plate with a line drawn on it that divides it into two equal parts. **What is the whole?** the entire plate **How many equal parts does the plate have?** 2 equal parts Explain that *halves* are two equal parts of a whole. Repeat with plates for three and four equal parts.

Literature Connection

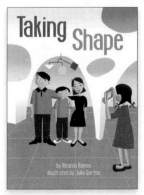

Taking Shape

From the Grab-and-Go™ Differentiated Centers Kit

Children read about combining shapes and seeing shapes within other shapes.

❶ ENGAGE

with the Interactive Student Edition

Essential Question
What are halves, thirds, and fourths of a whole?

Making Connections
Encourage children to think about cutting or folding things into equal parts.

How many parts do we have if we fold a piece of paper down the middle? 2 **What happens if we fold the paper in the middle again? How many parts do we have now?** 4 **How many parts do we have if we fold the paper down the middle one more time?** 8

Learning Activity
Guide the children to find two equal parts of a whole.

• **Why does Jessie want to cut the apple?** to make it easier to eat

• **How many equal parts does Jessie want to have?** two equal parts

• **What is Jessie trying to find out?** the special name for the two equal parts of a whole

• **What would happen if Jessie cut each part into 2 equal pieces?** Answers will vary.

Literacy and Mathematics
Choose one or more of the following activities.

• Ask the children to practice spelling half and halves, fourth and fourths, eighth and eighths. Point out the spelling for halves.

• Ask children to write a story similar to Jessie and the apple. Be sure the children cut the whole into equal pieces.

2 EXPLORE

Listen and Draw

Materials pattern blocks

Give children pattern blocks. After children read the directions, have them place a yellow hexagon on the workspace and make the same shape by using any combination of pattern blocks.

- **How can you tell whether the outline of the blocks you used is the same shape as the yellow hexagon?** Possible answer: I can put the blocks on top of the yellow hexagon and cover it.

- **Can you make the same shape as the hexagon using only one kind of pattern block? Explain.** Yes. Possible answers: 6 green triangles, 3 blue quadrilaterals, or 2 red quadrilaterals

- **Suppose you only have one of each kind of pattern block. Which pattern blocks could you use to make the hexagon shape?** Possible answers: 1 green triangle, 1 blue quadrilateral, and 1 red quadrilateral

 MP3 Construct viable arguments and critique the reasoning of others. Use **Math Talk** to focus on children's understanding of how to make a shape by using different combinations of smaller shapes.

ELL Strategy:
Cooperative Grouping

Pair fluent English speakers with English Learners.

- **Have children recognize a sheet of paper as a rectangle. Have children fold the rectangles into two equal parts.**

- **Discuss that these are called *halves*. Have children describe the halves.**

- **Repeat the activity having partners fold new rectangles into three equal parts (*thirds*) and four equal parts (*fourths*).**

 2.G.A.3 Partition circles and rectangles into two, three, or four equal shares, describe the shares using the words *halves, thirds, half of, a third of*, etc., and describe the whole as two halves, three thirds, four fourths. Recognize that equal shares of identical wholes need not have the same shape.

Name _____

Lesson 11.8

Equal Parts

Essential Question What are halves, thirds, and fourths of a whole?

 Geometry—2.G.A.3

MATHEMATICAL PRACTICES
MP3, MP6, MP8

Listen and Draw

Put pattern blocks together to match the shape of the hexagon. Trace the shape you made.

Check children's work.

Math Talk: Answers may vary. Check children's work.

FOR THE TEACHER • Have children place a yellow hexagon pattern block on the workspace and make the same shape by using any combination of pattern blocks. Discuss how they know if the outline of the blocks they used is the same shape as the yellow hexagon.

Math Talk

MATHEMATICAL PRACTICES 3

Compare models
Describe how the shapes you used are different from the shapes a classmate used.

Chapter 11

seven hundred forty-seven **747**

Differentiated Instruction

Reteach 11.8 ▲ RtI

Name _____

Lesson 11.8
Reteach

Equal Parts

You can divide a whole into equal parts.

2 equal parts	3 equal parts	4 equal parts
halves	thirds	fourths

Write how many equal parts there are in the whole.
Write halves, thirds, or fourths to name the equal parts.

1. __4__ equal parts   fourths
2. __2__ equal parts   halves
3. __3__ equal parts   thirds
4. __2__ equal parts   halves
5. __3__ equal parts   thirds
6. __4__ equal parts   fourths

Chapter Resources
11-19
Reteach

Enrich 11.8

Name _____

Lesson 11.8
Enrich

Shapes and Parts

Circle the shapes in each row that show the correct number of equal parts for each whole.

halves	
thirds	
fourths	

Writing and Reasoning Describe how you decided which shapes to circle for fourths.

Possible answer: I looked to see which shapes were divided into four equal parts.

Chapter Resources
11-20
Enrich

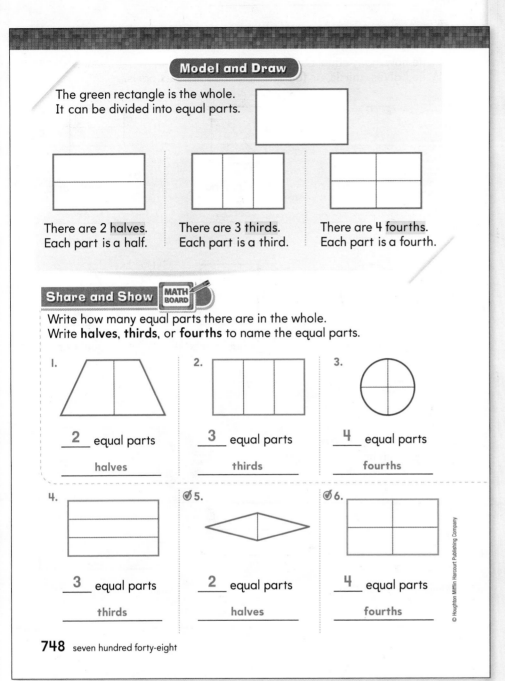

Model and Draw

The green rectangle is the whole.
It can be divided into equal parts.

There are 2 halves.
Each part is a half.

There are 3 thirds.
Each part is a third.

There are 4 fourths.
Each part is a fourth.

Share and Show MATH BOARD

Write how many equal parts there are in the whole.
Write **halves**, **thirds**, or **fourths** to name the equal parts.

1.
__2__ equal parts

halves

2.
__3__ equal parts

thirds

3.
__4__ equal parts

fourths

4.
__3__ equal parts

thirds

5.
__2__ equal parts

halves

6.
__4__ equal parts

fourths

© Houghton Mifflin Harcourt Publishing Company

748 seven hundred forty-eight

Advanced Learners
Kinesthetic / Logical / Mathematical
Individual / Partners

Materials construction paper

• Challenge children to use different shapes to illustrate equal parts.

• Ask children to fold or cut construction paper to model halves, thirds, and fourths. Remind children that to make halves, thirds, or fourths, the whole must be divided into parts that are equal in size.

• Have children share their shapes. Ask children to discuss how the various models of halves, thirds, and fourths are alike and different.

Model and Draw Common Core MATHEMATICAL PRACTICES
Discuss the model with children.

MP1 Make sense of problems and persevere in solving them.

• **Look at the different ways that the rectangle is divided into equal parts. How are the halves and the thirds different?**
Possible answer: Halves and thirds are both equal parts of a whole; halves are two equal parts that make up a whole and thirds are three equal parts that make up a whole.

• **How does the word *fourths* tell you the number of equal parts in the whole?**
Possible answer: *Fourths* has the word *four* in it.

❸ EXPLAIN

Share and Show MATH BOARD

Connect Exercises 1–6 to the learning model.

• **How can you decide if the equal parts are *halves*, *thirds*, or *fourths* of each whole?**
Possible answer: When there are two equal parts, the whole is divided into halves. When there are three equal parts, the whole is divided into thirds. When there are four equal parts, the whole is divided into fourths.

Use the checked exercises for **Quick Check.** Children should use their MathBoard to show their solutions to these exercises.

✔ Quick Check RtI

If ➤ a child misses the checked exercises

Then ➤ **Differentiate Instruction** with
  • Reteach 11.8
  • Personal Math trainer 2.G.A.3
  • RtI Tier 1 Activity (online)

⚠ COMMON ERRORS

Error Children may confuse halves, thirds, and fourths.

Example In Exercise 2, children identify that the shape has 3 equal parts, but do not write "thirds."

Springboard to Learning Have children compare the number words with the labels for equal parts. Help them see that **th**ree and **th**irds both start with **th** and **four**ths begins with the word **four**.

4 ELABORATE

On Your Own

If a child answers the checked exercises correctly, assign Exercises 7–13.

GO DEEPER

MP8 Look for and express regularity in repeated reasoning. To extend thinking, give each child three pieces of rectangular-shaped paper of the same size. Have children fold each piece into equal parts: one piece into halves, one piece into thirds, and one piece into fourths. Discuss with children how even though the rectangles were all folded differently, the wholes are all the same size. Then ask children to use the pieces of paper to compare the size of a half, a third, and a fourth.

THINK SMARTER

For Exercise 13, children must draw and explain what they know about halves. Use a piece of paper or diagram to refresh their memories if they struggle with the explanation.

Math on the Spot Video Tutor

Use this video to help children model and solve this type of *Think Smarter* problem.

GO DIGITAL **Math on the Spot** videos are in the Interactive Student Edition and at *www.thinkcentral.com*.

Name _____

On Your Own

Write how many equal parts there are in the whole.
Write **halves**, **thirds**, or **fourths** to name the equal parts.

7.

__2__ equal parts

__halves__

8.

__4__ equal parts

__fourths__

9.

__3__ equal parts

__thirds__

10.

__3__ equal parts

__thirds__

11.

__4__ equal parts

__fourths__

12.

__2__ equal parts

__halves__

13. **THINK SMARTER** Draw to show halves. Explain how you know that the parts are halves.
Possible answer: I drew a mark to show 2 equal parts. So, each part is a half.

Check children's work.

© Houghton Mifflin Harcourt Publishing Company

Problem Solving • Applications   WRITE) Math

14. **MATHEMATICAL PRACTICE 6** Make Connections Sort the shapes.

• Draw an X on shapes that do **not** show equal parts.

• Use red to color the shapes that show thirds.

• Use blue to color the shapes that show fourths.

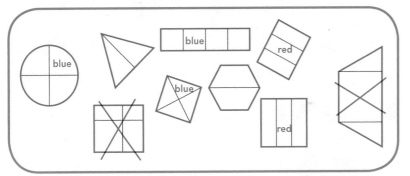

15. THINK SMARTER ✛ Draw lines to show fourths three different ways.

Personal Math Trainer

Explain how you know that the parts are fourths.

Possible answer: I drew lines to show 4 equal parts.

Each part is a fourth.

 TAKE HOME ACTIVITY • Ask your child to fold one sheet of paper into halves and another sheet of paper into fourths.

750 seven hundred fifty

© Houghton Mifflin Harcourt Publishing Company

Problem Solving • Applications

Common Core **MATHEMATICAL PRACTICES**

MP6 Attend to precision. If children have difficulty with Exercise 14, have them work in pairs to identify which shapes show thirds and which show fourths.

THINK SMARTER ✛

Personal Math Trainer

Be sure to assign this problem to children in the Personal Math Trainer. It features a video to help them model and answer the problem. This item assesses their abilities to complete a model to show fourths.

⑤ EVALUATE Formative Assessment

Essential Question

Reflect Using the Language Objective
Have children draw examples on their MathBoard to answer the Essential Question.

What are halves, thirds, and fourths of a whole? Possible answer: They are equal parts of a whole. Halves are two equal parts. Thirds are three equal parts. Fourths are four equal parts.

Math Journal WRITE) Math

Look at the shapes in Exercise 14. Describe the shapes that you did not color or draw an X on.

 DIFFERENTIATED INSTRUCTION INDEPENDENT ACTIVITIES

Grab-and-Go!™

Differentiated Centers Kit

Activities
Tank Full Toad

Children complete blue Activity Card 20 by using manipulatives to show fractions in thirds and halves.

Literature
Taking Shape

Children read about combining shapes and seeing shapes within other shapes.

Games
Hidden Figures

Children practice identifying two-dimensional figures within shapes.

Lesson 11.8 750

Practice and Homework

Use the Practice and Homework pages to provide children with more practice of the concepts and skills presented in this lesson. Children master their understanding as they complete practice items and then challenge their critical thinking skills with Problem Solving. Use the Write Math section to determine children's understanding of content for this lesson. Encourage children to use their Math Journals to record their answers.

Equal Parts

 COMMON CORE STANDARD—2.G.A.3
Reason with shapes and their attributes.

Write how many equal parts there are in the whole.
Write halves, thirds, or fourths to name the equal parts.

1.

__4__ equal parts
fourths

2.

__2__ equal parts
halves

3.

__3__ equal parts
thirds

 **Problem Solving** Real World

4. Sort the shapes.
   - Draw an X on the shapes that do not show equal parts.
   - Circle the shapes that show halves.

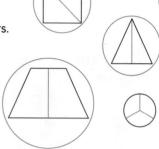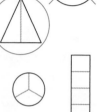

5. **WRITE** Math Look at the shapes in Exercise 4.
   Describe the shapes that you did not put an X on or circle.

   Check children's work. _____

   _____

   _____

Lesson Check (2.G.A.3)

1. What are the 3 equal parts of the shape called?

thirds

2. What are the 4 equal parts of the shape called?

fourths

Spiral Review (2.NBT.B.5, 2.G.A.1)

3. What is the sum?

$$\begin{array}{r} 87 \\ + 45 \\ \hline 132 \end{array}$$

4. What is the difference?

$$\begin{array}{r} 59 \\ - 15 \\ \hline 44 \end{array}$$

5. Circle the quadrilateral.

6. Circle the hexagon.

© Houghton Mifflin Harcourt Publishing Company

752 seven hundred fifty-two

FOR MORE PRACTICE
GO TO THE
Personal Math Trainer

Continue concepts and skills practice with Lesson Check. Use Spiral Review to engage children in previously taught concepts and to promote content retention. Common Core standards are correlated to each section.

Show Equal Parts of a Whole

LESSON AT A GLANCE

FOCUS **COHERENCE** **RIGOR**

F C R Focus:

 Common Core State Standards

2.G.A.3 Partition circles and rectangles into two, three, or four equal shares, describe the shares using the words *halves, thirds, half of, a third of,* etc., and describe the whole as two halves, three thirds, four fourths. Recognize that equal shares of identical wholes need not have the same shape.

MATHEMATICAL PRACTICES
MP5 Use appropriate tools strategically. **MP6** Attend to precision.

F C R Coherence:

Standards Across the Grades

Before	Grade 2	After
1.G.A.3	2.G.A.3	3.G.A.2

F C R Rigor:

Level 1: Understand Concepts.....................*Share and Show* (✓ Checked Items)
Level 2: Procedural Skills and Fluency.......*On Your Own*
Level 3: Applications...............................*Think Smarter and Go Deeper*

Learning Objective
Partition shapes to show halves, thirds, or fourths.

Language Objective
Children write an explanation in their Math Journal of how you know if a shape shows halves, thirds, or fourths.

Materials
MathBoard

F C R For more about how *GO Math!* fosters **Coherence** within the Content Standards and Mathematical Progressions for this chapter, see page 701J.

About the Math
Professional Development

Teaching for Depth

It is important for children to build a conceptual foundation about fractions so they can be prepared to use fractions in later grades. In the previous lesson, children identified equal parts of a whole. In this lesson, they apply this knowledge of equal parts as they divide a whole into equal parts of halves, thirds, and fourths.

Allow children to use blank fraction strips (see *eTeacher Resources*) to model a whole divided into equal parts. Children may cut out the fraction strips that show halves, thirds, and fourths, glue them to a poster board, and label them. Then children can use their posters as a visual aid.

 Professional Development Videos

 GO DIGITAL

 **Interactive Student Edition**

 **Personal Math Trainer**

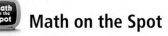 **Math on the Spot**

 **HMH Mega Math**

Daily Routines

Common Core

 Problem of the Day 11.9

Basic Facts

$7 + 2 = \underline{9}$ $3 + 7 = \underline{10}$

$8 - 2 = \underline{6}$ $6 - 3 = \underline{3}$

$6 + 1 = \underline{7}$ $2 + 9 = \underline{11}$

$8 - 3 = \underline{5}$ $9 - 1 = \underline{8}$

Vocabulary

 • **Interactive Student Edition**
• **Multimedia eGlossary**

Vocabulary Builder

Ask children what the name is for parts of a shape divided into:

• **2 equal parts**

• **3 equal parts**

• **4 equal parts**

① ENGAGE

with the Interactive Student Edition

Essential Question

How do you know if a shape shows halves, thirds, or fourths?

Making Connections

Invite children to think about parts of a whole.

What is some thing or object that you can share equally with a friend? Answers will vary. **What would it look like to divide the object into equal parts?** Answers will vary. **What would it look like if the parts were not equal?** Answers will vary.

Learning Activity

Guide the children to visualize 4 equal parts of a whole.

• **What does the word fourths mean?** 4 equal parts

• **Why do you think the dad wants to divide the cornbread into fourths?** He wants there to a piece for each person in the family.

Literacy and Mathematics

View the lesson opener with the children. Then, you can choose one or more of the following activities.

• Ask children to write a story that uses thirds or halves.

• Write halves, fourths, and thirds on the board, and ask children to write their meaning and draw an example.

② EXPLORE

Listen and Draw

Have children read the directions for the activity. Discuss that when parts of a whole are the same size, they are equal parts. Explain that the lines divide the shapes into parts. *Divide* in this case means "to separate."

Point to the rectangle at the top of the page.

* **Does this rectangle show equal parts? Explain.** No; the parts are not the same size.

Point to the circle at the top right of the page.

* **Does this circle show equal parts? Explain.** Yes; the two parts of the circle are the same size.

* **Do any of the shapes on the page show thirds? Explain.** No; none of the shapes show 3 equal parts.

* **Do any of the shapes on the page show fourths? Explain.** Yes; the square and the rectangle at the bottom of the page show 4 equal parts.

 MP6 Attend to precision. Use **Math Talk** to focus on children's understanding of showing equal parts of a whole.

ELL **Strategy:**
Model Concepts

Children better understand fraction concepts and vocabulary if they are modeled.

* **Draw 3 circles on the board. Divide them to show two, three, and four unequal parts.**

* **Draw circles showing halves, thirds, and fourths in equal parts.**

* **Use the circles to model equal and unequal parts.**

* **Ask: Which parts are *equal*? Which parts are *unequal*? Which circle shows *thirds*?**

* **Ask children to describe circles based on the number of parts.**

 2.G.A.3 Partition circles and rectangles into two, three, or four equal shares, describe the shares using the words *halves, thirds, half of, a third of,* etc., and describe the whole as two halves, three thirds, four fourths. Recognize that equal shares of identical wholes need not have the same shape.

Name _____

Show Equal Parts of a Whole
Essential Question How do you know if a shape shows halves, thirds, or fourths?

Lesson 11.9

Common Core Geometry—2.G.A.3

MATHEMATICAL PRACTICES
MP5, MP6

Listen and Draw

Circle the shapes that show equal parts.

Math Talk: No; Possible explanation: The two parts in the triangle are not equal in size, so the triangle does not show halves.

Math Talk MATHEMATICAL PRACTICES 6

Does the triangle show halves? **Explain.**

© Houghton Mifflin Harcourt Publishing Company

🏠 **HOME CONNECTION •** Your child completed this sorting activity with shapes to review the concept of equal parts.

Chapter 11

seven hundred fifty-three **753**

Reteach 11.9 ⚠ **RtI**

Name _____

Lesson 11.9
Reteach

Show Equal Parts of a Whole

Trace to show the equal parts.

| 2 equal parts | 3 equal parts | 4 equal parts |
| 2 halves | 3 thirds | 4 fourths |

Draw to show equal parts. **Check children's drawings.**

1. halves   2. thirds

3. halves   4. fourths

Chapter Resources
© Houghton Mifflin Harcourt Publishing Company

11-21

Reteach

Enrich 11.9 **Differentiated Instruction**

Name _____

Lesson 11.9
Enrich

Picture Equal Parts

Draw lines on each picture to show equal parts. **Check children's work.**

1. Show 2 equal parts.

2. Show 3 equal parts.

3. Show 4 equal parts.

🖊 **Writing and Reasoning** In Exercise 1, how did you decide how to show two equal parts on the heart shape?

Possible answer: I saw that the round parts of the heart were the same, so I drew a line down the center.

Chapter Resources
© Houghton Mifflin Harcourt Publishing Company

11-22

Enrich

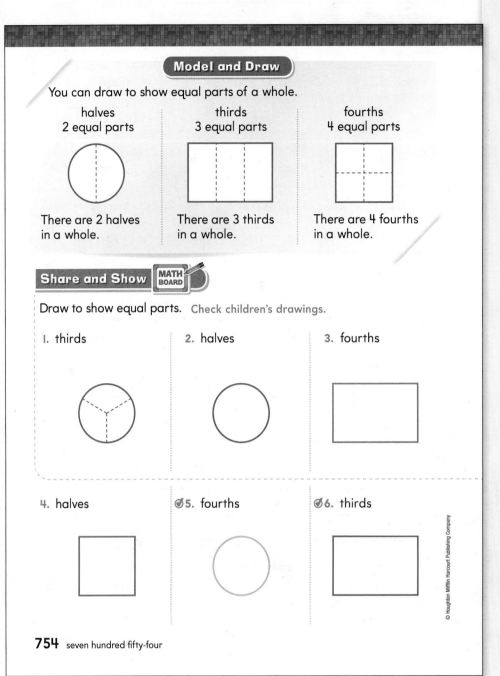

Model and Draw

You can draw to show equal parts of a whole.

halves 2 equal parts	thirds 3 equal parts	fourths 4 equal parts
There are 2 halves in a whole.	There are 3 thirds in a whole.	There are 4 fourths in a whole.

Share and Show

Draw to show equal parts. *Check children's drawings.*

1. thirds
2. halves
3. fourths

4. halves
✓5. fourths
✓6. thirds

© Houghton Mifflin Harcourt Publishing Company

Model and Draw  MATHEMATICAL PRACTICES

Work through the model with children. Have children trace over the dashed lines to divide the shapes into equal parts.

- **If you wanted to draw fourths on a circle, how many fourths would there be in the whole circle?** 4 fourths

MP1 Make sense of problems and persevere in solving them. Describe an object that has equal parts. Accept reasonable explanations.

③ EXPLAIN

Share and Show

Connect Exercises 1–6 to the learning model. You may wish to have children use some type of small straightedge when they draw to show equal parts for the shapes.

MP5 Use appropriate tools strategically.

- **How did you show fourths in Exercise 3?**
  Possible answer: I drew one line up and down and one line across the rectangle to make four equal parts.

Use the checked exercises for **Quick Check.** Children should use their MathBoard to show their solutions to these exercises.

 Quick Check  RtI

If	a child misses the checked exercises
Then	**Differentiate Instruction** with • Reteach 11.9 • Personal Math trainer 2.G.A.3 • RtI Tier 1 Activity (online)

! COMMON ERRORS

Error Children may confuse the number of lines that they use to divide a shape and the number of equal parts.

Example In Exercise 6, children draw 3 lines to divide the shape into thirds, which would show fourths.

Springboard to Learning Have children divide squares into two, three, and four equal parts. Guide children in counting the number of equal parts. Have them label their drawings.

Advanced Learners
Kinesthetic / Visual
Individual / Partners

Materials Fraction Circles (wholes, halves, thirds, fourths) (see *eTeacher Resources*), construction paper, crayons, scissors, glue

- Have children cut apart whole fraction circles to show two unequal parts, three unequal parts, and four unequal parts.
- Then have them cut apart the halves, thirds, and fourths fraction circles to show equal parts.
- Have children shuffle all the parts of all the circles and spread them out.
- Have children find equal parts and glue them to construction paper to make an "Equal Parts" poster. Children should only include equal parts in their design.
- Allow children to color their posters and present them to the class.

On Your Own

If a child answers the checked exercises correctly, assign Exercises 7–16. If children found it helpful for Exercises 1–6, you may wish to again have children use some type of small straightedge when they draw to show equal parts for the shapes.

Materials Circles, Rectangles, Squares (different sizes) (see *eTeacher Resources*)

MP6 Attend to precision. To extend thinking, have children make a poster to show equal parts of different shapes. Distribute cutouts of different-sized circles and rectangles, including squares. Have children trace and cut out these shapes. Then have them draw on the shapes to show equal parts. Suggest that children only show halves and fourths on the circles. Ask children to glue the shapes to a poster board or chart paper and label how many equal parts of the whole each shape shows. Finally, have children write about the equal parts that make up each whole.

Name _____

On Your Own

Draw to show equal parts. Check children's drawings.

7. halves

8. fourths

9. thirds

10. thirds

11. halves

12. fourths

13. halves

14. thirds

15. fourths

16. Does this shape show thirds? Explain.

No; Possible explanation: The shape has parts

that are not equal in size. The 3 parts must be

equal in size to show thirds.

_____

© Houghton Mifflin Harcourt Publishing Company

Problem Solving • Applications   WRITE Math

17. Colton and three friends want to share a pizza equally. Draw to show how the pizza should be divided.

18. **GO DEEPER** There are two square pizzas. Each pizza is cut into fourths. How many pieces of pizza are there?

_____8_____ pieces

19. **THINK SMARTER** Fill in the bubble next to the shapes that show thirds. Explain your answer.

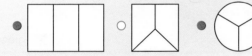

The shapes with three parts that are equal in

size are divided into thirds.

 TAKE HOME ACTIVITY • Have your child describe how to show equal parts of a shape.

756 seven hundred fifty-six

DIFFERENTIATED INSTRUCTION   INDEPENDENT ACTIVITIES

 Grab-and-Go!™

Differentiated Centers Kit

Activities
Tank Full Toad

Children complete blue Activity Card 20 by using manipulatives to show fractions in thirds and halves.

Literature
Taking Shape

Children read about combining shapes and seeing shapes within other shapes.

Games
Hidden Figures

Children practice identifying two-dimensional figures within shapes.

Problem Solving • Applications

Common Core **MATHEMATICAL PRACTICES**

Have children read Exercises 17 and 18.

 Math on the Spot Video Tutor
Use this video to help children model and solve this type of *Think Smarter* problem.

GO DIGITAL **Math on the Spot** videos are in the Interactive Student Edition and at *www.thinkcentral.com*.

GO DEEPER

MP6 Attend to precision. In Exercise 18, children use higher order thinking skills to find the number of fourths in two squares. Have children share how they solved the problem.

THINK SMARTER

Children will need to be able to recognize a model showing thirds. They should understand that the sizes of the three pieces of the model must be equal for the model to show thirds. Children who select all of the answer choices likely are only counting the number of pieces, without considering whether those pieces are equal.

5 EVALUATE   Formative Assessment

Essential Question

Reflect Using the Language Objective Have children write an explanation in their Math Journal to answer the Essential Question.

How do you know if a shape shows halves, thirds, or fourths? Possible answer: If a shape has 2 equal parts, it shows halves. If it has 3 equal parts, it shows thirds. If it has 4 equal parts, it shows fourths.

Math Journal  Math

Draw three rectangles. Then draw to show halves, thirds, and fourths. Write about each whole that you have drawn.

Lesson 11.9 756

Practice and Homework

Use the Practice and Homework pages to provide children with more practice of the concepts and skills presented in this lesson. Children master their understanding as they complete practice items and then challenge their critical thinking skills with Problem Solving. Use the Write Math section to determine children's understanding of content for this lesson. Encourage children to use their Math Journals to record their answers.

Name _____

Show Equal Parts of a Whole

COMMON CORE STANDARD—2.G.A.3
Reason with shapes and their attributes.

Draw to show equal parts. Check children's drawings.

1. halves

2. fourths

3. thirds

4. thirds

5. halves

6. fourths

Problem Solving Real World

Solve. Write or draw to explain.

7. Joe has one sandwich. He cuts the sandwich into fourths. How many pieces of sandwich does he have?

____4____ pieces

8. **WRITE** Math Draw three rectangles. Then draw to show halves, thirds, and fourths. Write about each whole that you have drawn.

Check children's work.

© Houghton Mifflin Harcourt Publishing Company

Lesson Check (2.G.A.3)

1. Circle the shape divided into fourths.

   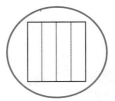

Spiral Review (2.MD.A.4, 2.G.A.1)

2. How many angles does this shape have?

   __5__ angles

3. How many faces does a rectangular prism have?

   __6__ faces

4. Use a centimeter ruler. Measure the length of each object. How much longer is the ribbon than the string?

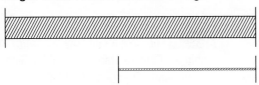

   __5__ centimeters longer

© Houghton Mifflin Harcourt Publishing Company

FOR MORE PRACTICE
GO TO THE
Personal Math Trainer

Continue concepts and skills practice with Lesson Check. Use Spiral Review to engage children in previously taught concepts and to promote content retention. Common Core standards are correlated to each section.

Describe Equal Parts

LESSON AT A GLANCE

FOCUS **COHERENCE** **RIGOR**

F C R Focus:

 Common Core State Standards

2.G.A.3 Partition circles and rectangles into two, three, or four equal shares, describe the shares using the words halves, thirds, half of, a third of, etc., and describe the whole as two halves, three thirds, four fourths. Recognize that equal shares of identical wholes need not have the same shape.

MATHEMATICAL PRACTICES
MP3 Construct viable arguments and critique the reasoning of others. **MP4** Model with Mathematics. **MP6** Attend to precision.

F C R Coherence:

Standards Across the Grades

Before	Grade 2	After
1.G.A.3	2.G.A.3	3.G.A.2

F C R Rigor:

Level 1: Understand Concepts....................*Share and Show* (✓ Checked Items)
Level 2: Procedural Skills and Fluency.......*On Your Own*
Level 3: Applications................................*Think Smarter and Go Deeper*

Learning Objective

Identify and describe one equal part as a half of, a third of, or a fourth of a whole.

Language Objective

Child partners develop a step-by-step instruction sheet for new children on how you know if a shape shows halves, thirds, or fourths.

Materials

MathBoard, green and red crayons

F C R For more about how *GO Math!* fosters **Coherence** within the Content Standards and Mathematical Progressions for this chapter, see page 701J.

About the Math
Professional Development

Teaching for Depth

This lesson allows children to explore and demonstrate their understanding of a *half of, a third of*, and a *fourth of*. The term *quarter of* is also introduced in this lesson. Learning this term now builds a foundation for the use of this term in later grades when telling time in different ways. Children construct these parts by dividing and coloring two-dimensional shapes.

• During and after the activity, ask children to describe what they have done for the different exercise sets.

• Throughout the school day, model using fraction terms in real-life situations and also give children opportunities to use fraction terms in context.

 Professional Development Videos

 **Interactive Student Edition**

 **Personal Math Trainer**

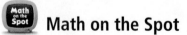 **Math on the Spot**

Daily Routines
Common Core

 Problem of the Day 11.10

Number of the Day 50¢

How many of each of these coins is equal to 50¢?

<u> 50 </u> pennies

<u> 2 </u> quarters

<u> 5 </u> dimes

<u> 10 </u> nickels

Vocabulary half of, third of, fourth of, quarter of

GO DIGITAL
• Interactive Student Edition
• Multimedia eGlossary

Fluency Builder
Basic Facts

Common Core Fluency Standard 2.0A.B.2

Subtract.

1. $9 - 2 = $ <u> 7 </u>

2. $6 - 4 = $ <u> 2 </u>

3. $8 - 4 = $ <u> 4 </u>

4. $14 - 7 = $ <u> 7 </u>

5. $5 - 5 = $ <u> 0 </u>

6. $17 - 9 = $ <u> 8 </u>

7. $13 - 6 = $ <u> 7 </u>

8. $16 - 9 = $ <u> 7 </u>

① ENGAGE

with the Interactive Student Edition

Essential Question
How do you find a half of, a third of, or a fourth of a whole?

Making Connections
Ask children to explain what they know about two-dimensional shapes divided into equal parts.

How would you draw a square divided into four equal parts? Accept any accurate drawing. **How would you draw a circle divided into four equal parts?** Accept only drawings that show two diameters crossing at right angles. **What do you call parts of a shape divided into two equal parts? Three equal parts?** halves; thirds

Learning Activity
What is the problem the children are trying to solve? Connect the story to the problem. Ask the following questions.

• **What are the children in the problem trying to do?** Check children's work.

• **What do Jessie and Okena want to find out?** what a fourth of a circle looks like

Literacy and Mathematics
View the lesson opener with the children. Then, choose one or more of the following activities:

• Have children write a story about dividing a shape or real world object into equal parts. Have them draw a picture to accompany their story.

• Have children identify times in their lives where they have divided objects into equal parts, for example, sharing an apple with a friend.

2 EXPLORE

Listen and Draw

Materials green and red crayons

Have children look at the shapes on the page.

- **Do all the shapes show equal parts? Explain.** Yes. Possible explanation: In each shape, all of the parts are the same size.

Have children read the directions for this activity.

- **How many equal parts of a whole show fourths?** 4 equal parts
- **How many equal parts of a whole show halves?** 2 equal parts

Have children color the shapes that show fourths green and the shapes that show halves red.

- **Which shapes did you color green? Describe them.** Possible answer: One is a square, and one is a circle. They both show fourths.
- **Which shapes did you color red? Describe them.** Possible answer: One is a rectangle, and one is a circle. They both show halves.

 **MP3 Construct viable arguments and critique the reasoning of others.** Use Math Talk to focus on children's understanding that the size and shape of equal parts can be different for different shapes.

ELL Strategy:
Illustrate Understanding

Draw 3 rectangles. Divide one into halves, one into thirds, and one into fourths. Shade one part of each rectangle.

- Write *a half of, a third of,* and *a fourth of* in a word bank.
- Point to a rectangle and then to the corresponding words in the word bank.
- Write and say: This rectangle has _____ equal parts. The shading shows _____ the rectangle.
- In pairs, have children follow your model. They should draw and label each picture.

 2.G.A.3 Partition circles and rectangles into two, three, or four equal shares, describe the shares using the words *halves, thirds, half of, a third of,* etc., and describe the whole as two halves, three thirds, four fourths. Recognize that equal shares of identical wholes need not have the same shape.

Name _____

Lesson 11.10

Describe Equal Parts

Essential Question How do you find a half of, a third of, or a fourth of a whole?

Common Core Geometry—2.G.A.3

MATHEMATICAL PRACTICES
MP3, MP4, MP6

Listen and Draw

Find shapes that show fourths and color them green.
Find shapes that show halves and color them red.

Math Talk: Check children's understanding of the fact that in different shapes the size and the shape of the parts can be different.

Math Talk MATHEMATICAL PRACTICES **3**

Describe how the thirds in the unshaded shapes compare to each other.

HOME CONNECTION • Your child identified the number of equal parts in shapes to review describing equal parts of a whole.

Chapter 11

seven hundred fifty-nine **759**

© Houghton Mifflin Harcourt Publishing Company

Reteach 11.10 ▲RtI

Name _____

Lesson 11.10
Reteach

Describe Equal Parts

One equal part of each shape is shaded.

A half of the shape is shaded. A third of the shape is shaded. A fourth of the shape is shaded.

Draw to show halves. Check children's work.
Color a half of the shape.

1. 2.

Draw to show fourths. Check children's work.
Color a fourth of the shape.

3. 4.

Chapter Resources 11-23 Reteach

Enrich 11.10 **Differentiated Instruction**

Name _____

Lesson 11.10
Enrich

Garden Plots

A farmer has 2 gardens that are the same size.
A third of one garden is fruit.
A fourth of the other garden is flowers.
The rest of both gardens are vegetables.

Draw to show each garden divided into equal parts. Check children's work.

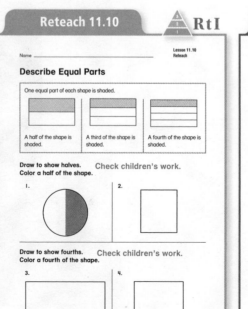

Color each part.

1. Use orange to show fruit.
2. Use blue to show flowers.
3. Use green to show vegetables.

Writing and Reasoning Did the farmer plant more fruit or flowers? Explain.

Possible answer: The farmer planted more fruit. One third of a garden is larger than one fourth of the same-sized garden.

Chapter Resources 11-24 Enrich

Model and Draw

These are some ways to show and describe an equal part of a whole.

I of 4 equal parts is called a **quarter of** that shape.

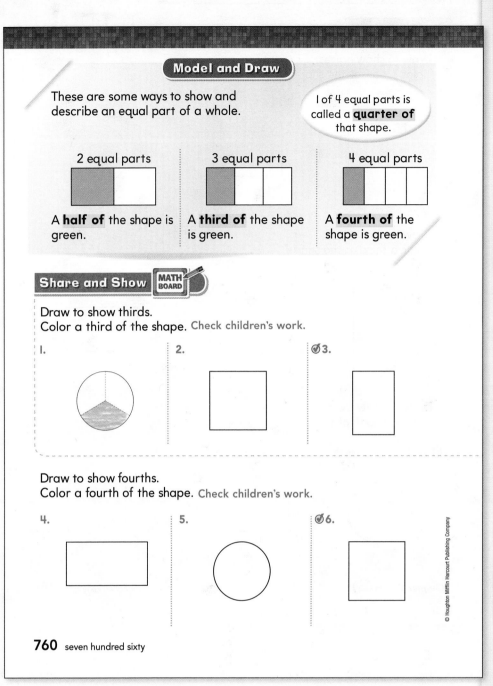

2 equal parts

A **half of** the shape is green.

3 equal parts

A **third of** the shape is green.

4 equal parts

A **fourth of** the shape is green.

Share and Show MATH BOARD

Draw to show thirds.
Color a third of the shape. Check children's work.

1.

2.

⌀3.

Draw to show fourths.
Color a fourth of the shape. Check children's work.

4.

5.

⌀6.

© Houghton Mifflin Harcourt Publishing Company

Advanced Learners — Kinesthetic / Interpersonal / Social Partners

Materials assorted Plane Shapes (see *eTeacher Resources*), crayons, rulers or other straightedges

- Give children an assortment of plane shapes.
- Have them divide the shapes into two, three, and four equal parts. Then have them color one part of each shape.
- Have children shuffle together the shapes and lay them facedown in rows.
- Children then take turns playing a matching game in which they turn over two shapes and determine if the shapes show the same type of equal parts of a whole. If they do, the child takes the shapes.
- Play continues until as many pairs as possible have been made.

Model and Draw  MATHEMATICAL PRACTICES

MP4 Model with mathematics. Work through the model with children. Point out that *a quarter of* and *a fourth of* have the same meaning. Both describe one out of four equal parts. Discuss that even though only one part of each shape is shaded, each shape is divided into equal parts.

- **How many parts are green in each shape?**
  1 part
- **How many parts are not green in the first shape?** 1 part, or a half of the shape

❸ EXPLAIN

Share and Show MATH BOARD

Connect Exercises 1–6 to the learning model. You may wish to have children use a small straightedge when they draw to show equal parts for the shapes.

- **How many parts do you color in each shape?** 1 part

Use the checked exercise for **Quick Check**. Children should use their MathBoard to show their solutions to these exercises.

✔ Quick Check   RtI

If ➤ a child misses the checked exercises

Then ➤ **Differentiate Instruction** with
- Reteach 11.10
- Personal Math trainer 2.G.A.3
- RtI Tier 1 Activity (online)

⚠ COMMON ERRORS

Error Children do not divide the shape into the right number of equal parts.

Example In Exercise 2, children divide the square into halves.

Springboard to Learning Remind children that to show a third of a whole, there must be 3 equal parts and to show a fourth of a whole, there must be 4 equal parts. After children draw to show thirds or fourths, have them count the equal parts of the whole.

On Your Own

MP6 Attend to precision. If a child answers the checked exercises correctly, assign Exercises 7–15. Remind children to only color one of the equal parts.

Materials clock faces

Display a clock face. Elicit from children that the face of a clock has the shape of a circle. Explain that you can show parts of a whole on a clock face. Move the minute hand around the clock, starting at 12 and ending back at 12. Explain that one hour is the whole.

Shade a quarter of the clock face, inside the lines going from the center of the clock to the 12 and to the 3. Point to demonstrate the movement of the minute hand from the 12 to the 3. Explain that this movement of the minute hand shows a quarter of an hour. Then repeat the activity for a half of an hour by shading the right half of the clock face.

Name _____

On Your Own

Draw to show halves.   Check children's work.
Color a half of the shape.

7.

8.

9.

Draw to show thirds.
Color a third of the shape.   Check children's work.

10.

11.

12.

Draw to show fourths.
Color a fourth of the shape.   Check children's work.

13.

14.

15.

© Houghton Mifflin Harcourt Publishing Company

Chapter 11 • Lesson 10   seven hundred sixty-one **761**

Problem Solving • Applications

WRITE Math

16. *THINK SMARTER* Two posters are the same size. A third of one poster is red, and a fourth of the other poster is blue.

Is the red part or the blue part larger? Draw and write to explain.

Check children's work.

the red part; Possible explanation: The

poster divided into thirds has 3 equal parts.

The poster divided into fourths has 4 equal

parts. A third of a poster is larger than a

fourth of a poster that is the same size.

17. *THINK SMARTER* Draw to show halves, thirds, and fourths. Color a half of, a third of, or a fourth of the shape.

Check children's work.

© Houghton Mifflin Harcourt Publishing Company

 TAKE HOME ACTIVITY • Draw a square. Have your child draw to show thirds and color a third of the square.

762 seven hundred sixty-two

DIFFERENTIATED INSTRUCTION | **INDEPENDENT ACTIVITIES**

Differentiated Centers Kit

Activities
Tank Full Toad

Children complete blue Activity Card 20 by using manipulatives to show fractions in thirds and halves.

Literature
Taking Shape

Children read about combining shapes and seeing shapes within other shapes.

Problem Solving • Applications

Common Core **MATHEMATICAL PRACTICES**

THINK SMARTER

MP6 Attend to precision. In Exercise 16, children use higher order thinking skills to compare a third of and a fourth of the same-sized shape to determine which is larger.

 Math on the Spot Video Tutor

Use this video to help children model and solve this type of *Think Smarter* problem.

 Math on the Spot videos are in the Interactive **DIGITAL** Student Edition and at *www.thinkcentral.com*.

THINK SMARTER

This item assesses children's abilities to draw equal parts. Children will first need to ensure that their models are divided into equal parts and then to interpret the fraction name by shading one part of the shape.

⑤ EVALUATE Formative Assessment

Essential Question

Reflect Using the Language Objective Have children write an explanation in their Math Journal to answer the Essential Question.

How do you find a half of, a third of, or a fourth of a whole? Possible answer: For a half of a shape, I divided the shape into 2 equal parts and shaded 1 part. For a third of a shape, I divided the shape into 3 equal parts and shaded 1 part. For a fourth of a shape, I divided the shape into 4 equal parts and shaded 1 part.

Math Journal  Math

Draw pictures to show a third of a whole and a fourth of a whole. Label each picture.

Lesson 11.10 762

Practice and Homework

Use the Practice and Homework pages to provide children with more practice of the concepts and skills presented in this lesson. Children master their understanding as they complete practice items and then challenge their critical thinking skills with Problem Solving. Use the Write Math section to determine children's understanding of content for this lesson. Encourage children to use their Math Journals to record their answers.

Name _____

Describe Equal Parts

COMMON CORE STANDARD—2.G.A.3
Reason with shapes and their attributes.

Draw to show halves.
Color a half of the shape. Check children's work.

1.

2.

Draw to show thirds.
Color a third of the shape.

3.

4.

Problem Solving Real World

5. Circle all the shapes that have a third of the shape shaded.

6. **WRITE Math** Draw pictures to show a third of a whole and a fourth of a whole. Label each picture.

Check children's work.

© Houghton Mifflin Harcourt Publishing Company

Lesson Check (2.G.A.3)

1. Circle the shape that has a half of the shape shaded.

Spiral Review (2.MD.A.1, 2.MD.C.7, 2.G.A.1)

2. What is the name of this shape?

_____hexagon_____

3. Use a centimeter ruler. What is the length of the string to the nearest centimeter?

__6__ centimeters

4. The clock shows the time Chris finished his homework. Write the time. Then circle a.m. or p.m.

__6__ : __10__   a.m.
(p.m.)

5. What time is shown on this clock?

__8__ : __15__

FOR MORE PRACTICE
GO TO THE
Personal Math Trainer

© Houghton Mifflin Harcourt Publishing Company

Continue concepts and skills practice with Lesson Check. Use Spiral Review to engage children in previously taught concepts and to promote content retention. Common Core standards are correlated to each section.

Problem Solving • Equal Shares

FOCUS COHERENCE RIGOR
LESSON AT A GLANCE

F C R Focus:

 Common Core State Standards

2.G.A.3 Partition circles and rectangles into two, three, or four equal shares, describe the shares using the words *halves, thirds, half of, a third of,* etc., and describe the whole as two halves, three thirds, four fourths. Recognize that equal shares of identical wholes need not have the same shape.

MATHEMATICAL PRACTICES
MP1 Make sense of problems and persevere in solving them. **MP2** Reason abstractly and quantitatively. **MP4** Model with Mathematics. **MP6** Attend to precision.

F C R Coherence:

Standards Across the Grades
Before	Grade 2	After
1.G.A.3	2.G.A.3	3.G.A.2

F C R Rigor:

Level 1: Understand Concepts....................*Share and Show* (✓ Checked Items)
Level 2: Procedural Skills and Fluency.......*On Your Own*
Level 3: Applications..................................*Think Smarter and Go Deeper*

Learning Objective
Solve problems involving wholes divided into equal shares by using the strategy draw a diagram.

Language Objective
Children demonstrate and explain how drawing a diagram can help when solving problems about equal shares.

Materials
MathBoard

F C R For more about how *GO Math!* fosters **Coherence** within the Content Standards and Mathematical Progressions for this chapter, see page 701J.

About the Math
Professional Development

Model with mathematics.

Continued use of models while developing fraction concepts helps children have a visual representation to which they can refer. It is very helpful to show through modeling that equal shares of identical wholes do not need to be the same shape. The basic understanding children must acquire is, for example, that when two identical wholes are cut into halves, each half is the same size as all the other halves, even if they are a different shape.

First, verify that the two wholes are the same size. Then show the wholes divided into halves in different ways. Demonstrate for children that when either pair of equal-sized parts are put together, they make wholes that are the same size. Do this with different equal parts (halves, fourths, and thirds) and repeat the action as many times as necessary for children to understand.

Finally, have pairs of children use models to demonstrate to each other their understanding of the concept.

 Professional Development Videos

 **Interactive Student Edition**

 **Personal Math Trainer**

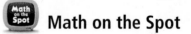 **Math on the Spot**

Daily Routines
Common Core

 Problem of the Day 11.11

Number of the Day 100

- Start with 100. Count by hundreds to 1,000.
- Start with 100. Count by tens to 340.
- Start with 100. Count by fives to 225.

Vocabulary

GO DIGITAL
- Interactive Student Edition
- Multimedia eGlossary

Fluency Builder
Mental Math

| Common Core Fluency Standard 2.OA.B.2 |

Add.

1. 2 + 5 = ___7___

2. 6 + 1 = ___7___

3. 4 + 3 = ___7___

4. 0 + 7 = ___7___

Add 10 to each number. What is the new number?

5. 19 29

6. 37 47

7. 80 90

8. 3 13

① ENGAGE

with the Interactive Student Edition

Essential Question
How can drawing a diagram help when solving problems about equal shares?

Making Connections
Ask children to explain what they know about two-dimensional shapes divided into equal parts.

How would you draw a rectangle divided into four equal parts? Accept any accurate drawing. **How would you draw a square divided into three equal parts?** Accept any accurate drawing. **What do you call parts of a shape divided into four equal parts? Two equal parts?** fourths; halves

Learning Activity
What is the problem the children are trying to solve? Connect the story to the problem. Ask the following questions.

- **What are the children in the problem trying to do?** The children are trying to cut the sandwiches into equal shares.

- **If there are 4 children, how many equal parts does there need to be?** 4

Literacy and Mathematics
View the lesson opener with the children. Then, choose one or more of the following activities:

- Have children write a story about dividing a shape or real world object into equal shares. Have them draw a picture to accompany their story.

- Have children identify times in their lives where they have divided objects into equal shares, for example, sharing a granola bar with a friend.

EXPLORE

Unlock the Problem

After reading the problem with children, work through the Problem Solving Graphic Organizer together. Discuss what children need to find and what information they need to use.

- **What are you asked to find?** two ways the sandwiches might be cut

- **What information do you need to use?** There are 2 sandwiches. Each sandwich is divided into fourths.

- **What does it mean that the sandwiches are divided into fourths?** Possible answer: It means that each sandwich is divided into 4 equal parts.

Point out that the squares on the page represent the two different sandwiches.

- **Use the squares as a diagram to help you solve the problem. Draw lines on the squares to show two ways the sandwiches might be cut into fourths.**

- **How can you show fourths in two different ways using the squares?** Possible answer: In the first square, I can draw one vertical line and one horizontal line dividing the square into 4 equal parts. In the second square I can draw 2 diagonal lines to show 4 equal parts that are different shapes than the fourths in the other square.

- **How are the squares alike? How are they different?** Possible answer: The squares both show 4 equal parts. The parts in one square are a different shape than the parts in the other square.

ELL **Strategy:**
Identify Relationships

Children connect prior knowledge about fractions to language and concepts studied in this chapter.

- **Say:** Every day we see things that are divided into *equal* pieces.

- **What have you seen that has been divided into halves? thirds? fourths?**

- **Have children draw a picture of something they have seen.**

- **Instruct them to draw another way to divide the item up into *equal* parts.**

- **Have children describe their drawings based on the number of equal parts.**

2.G.A.3 Partition circles and rectangles into two, three, or four equal shares, describe the shares using the words *halves, thirds, half of, a third of,* etc., and describe the whole as two halves, three thirds, four fourths. Recognize that equal shares of identical wholes need not have the same shape.

Name _____

Problem Solving • Equal Shares

**PROBLEM SOLVING
Lesson 11.11**

Essential Question How can drawing a diagram help when solving problems about equal shares?

Common Core Geometry—2.G.A.3

MATHEMATICAL PRACTICES
MP1, MP4, MP6

There are two sandwiches that are the same size. Each sandwich is divided into fourths, but the sandwiches are cut differently. How might the two sandwiches be cut?

Unlock the Problem

What do I need to find?
how the sandwiches could be cut

What information do I need to use?
There are __2__ sandwiches. Each sandwich is divided into __fourths__.

Show how to solve the problem. Possible answers are given.

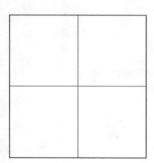 

 HOME CONNECTION • Your child drew a diagram to represent and solve a problem about dividing a whole in different ways to show equal shares.

Chapter 11   seven hundred sixty-five **765**

Reteach 11.11 ⚠ **RtI**

Name _____

Lesson 11.11
Reteach

Problem Solving • Equal Shares

Two gardens are the same size. Each garden is divided into halves, but the gardens are divided differently. How might the gardens be divided?

Unlock the Problem

What do I need to find?
how the gardens are divided

What information do I need to use?
There are __2__ gardens. Each garden is divided into __halves__

Show how to solve the problem.

Draw to show your answer. Possible answers are given.

1. Sophie has two pieces of paper that are the same size. She wants to divide each piece into fourths. What are two different ways she can divide the pieces of paper?

Chapter Resources   11-25   Reteach

Enrich 11.11 **Differentiated Instruction**

Name _____

Lesson 11.11
Enrich

Egg-Carton Shares

Draw to make equal parts for the eggs in both kinds of cartons.

Check children's drawings. Possible answers are shown.

1. Draw to show halves.

2. Draw to show thirds.

3. Draw to show fourths.

Writing and Reasoning How many eggs are in a half of a carton no matter how you divide it? Explain.

6 eggs are in a half of a carton. Possible answer:
Halves are 2 equal parts. So, 12 eggs in 2 equal parts is 6 eggs in each part.

Chapter Resources   11-26   Enrich

Try Another Problem

Draw to show your answer.

Check children's work. Possible answers are given.

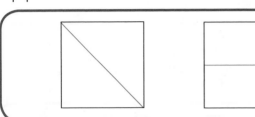
- What do I need to find?
- What information do I need to use?

1. Marquis has two square sheets of paper that are the same size. He wants to cut each sheet into halves. What are two different ways he can cut the sheets of paper?

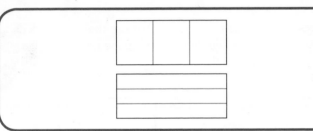

2. Shanice has two pieces of cloth that are the same size. She needs to divide each piece into thirds. What are two different ways she can divide the pieces of cloth?

Math Talk: Possible answer: A third of each piece of cloth is one of three equal parts. These two thirds (parts) are different shapes.

 Math Talk   MATHEMATICAL PRACTICES

In Problem 2, **explain** how a third of the two pieces of cloth are alike and how they are different.

© Houghton Mifflin Harcourt Publishing Company

Try Another Problem

Use questions to guide children through the first problem.

- **What do you need to find?** two ways to cut the sheets of paper into halves

- **What information do you need to use?** Marquis has two square sheets of paper. He wants to cut each sheet into halves.

- **How can you use the squares to help you solve the problem?** Possible answer: I can use the squares to show the two sheets of paper. I can draw lines to show two ways to divide the squares into halves.

- **How many equal parts should each square show?** 2 equal parts

- **How should the squares be different?** Possible answers: The squares should be divided into halves differently. The shape of the halves of one square should be different from the shape of the halves of the other square.

Repeat with a similar discussion for the second problem.

 Math Talk **MP1 Make sense of problems and persevere in solving them.** Use **Math Talk** to focus on children's understanding of how two identical shapes can show the same number of equal parts but the equal parts can look different.

 You may suggest that children place a completed Try Another Problem in their portfolios.

! COMMON ERRORS

Error Children do not know how to use the diagram to show two different ways to divide the shapes.

Example In Exercise 2, children draw two vertical lines to divide both rectangles into thirds in the same way.

Springboard to Learning Have children trace the shape several times onto another sheet of paper and cut out the shapes. After they draw on one of the shapes to show one way to divide it, have them fold it along the lines they drew. Then have them fold another shape to help them see another way to divide it. They can compare the folded shapes to determine if the shapes of the halves, thirds, or fourths are different.

Advanced Learners   🕐 Kinesthetic / Visual   Individual / Partners

Materials Plane Shapes, Triangles, Rectangles (see eTeacher Resources)

- Give children copies of squares, triangles, ovals, and circles. Have children divide each shape into halves.

- Then have children repeat the activity by dividing non-square rectangles into fourths in more than one way.

- Encourage children to share their drawings of each type of shape with each other to explore the different ways the shape can be divided to show halves and fourths.

- Have pairs take turns telling story problems about their divided shapes. Encourage them to share their story problems with the class.

③ EXPLAIN

Share and Show

Have children draw lines on the shapes to illustrate two ways that they can divide the shapes showing halves, thirds, or fourths.

Use the checked exercises for **Quick Check**. Children should use their MathBoard to show their solutions to these exercises.

 Quick Check

If ▶ a child misses the checked exercises

Then ▶ **Differentiate Instruction** with
- Reteach 11.11
- Personal Math Trainer 2.G.A.3
- RtI Tier 1 Activity (online)

MP2 Reason abstractly and quantitatively. To extend thinking, have children write a story problem about dividing a rectangle into halves, thirds, or fourths. Have volunteers share their problems with the class.

Encourage children to think creatively about the different ways the ribbons can be divided into thirds.

 Math on the Spot Video Tutor

 Use this video to help children model and solve this type of *Think Smarter* problem.

 Math on the Spot videos are in the Interactive Student Edition and at *www.thinkcentral.com*.

Name _____

Share and Show MATH BOARD

Draw to show your answer.

Check children's work.
Possible answers are given.

✓3. Brandon has two pieces of toast that are the same size. What are two different ways he can divide the pieces of toast into halves?

✓4. Mr. Rivera has two small trays of pasta that are the same size. What are two different ways he can cut the pasta into fourths?

5. THINK SMARTER Erin has two ribbons that are the same size. What are two different ways she can divide the ribbons into thirds?

© Houghton Mifflin Harcourt Publishing Company

Chapter 11 • Lesson 11   seven hundred sixty-seven **767**

Problem Solving • Applications (Real World) WRITE Math

Solve. Write or draw to explain.

6. **MATHEMATICAL PRACTICE 4** Use Diagrams David needs to divide two pieces of paper into the same number of equal parts. Look at how the first piece of paper is divided. Show how to divide the second piece of paper a different way. **Check children's work.**

7. **GO DEEPER** Mrs. Lee has two sandwiches that are the same size. She cuts each sandwich into halves. How many equal parts does she have in all?

___4___ equal parts

8. **THINK SMARTER** Emma wants to cut a piece of paper into fourths. Fill in the bubble next to all the ways she could cut the paper.

 TAKE HOME ACTIVITY • Ask your child to draw two rectangles and show two different ways to divide them into fourths.

768 seven hundred sixty-eight

© Houghton Mifflin Harcourt Publishing Company

DIFFERENTIATED INSTRUCTION   INDEPENDENT ACTIVITIES

Differentiated Centers Kit

Activities
Tank Full Toad

 Children complete blue Activity Card 20 by using manipulatives to show fractions in thirds and halves.

Literature
Taking Shape

 Children read about combining shapes and seeing shapes within other shapes.

---

4 ELABORATE

Problem Solving • Applications (Real World)

Explain to children that they may use any strategy or method to solve these problems.

MP4 Model with mathematics. Encourage children to think creatively about how to divide the second square. If students easily solve the problem, challenge them to find a third way to divide the square into fourths.

GO DEEPER

In Exercise 7, children use higher order thinking skills to find the number of equal shares in two sandwiches. Children may find it helpful to draw the sandwiches.

THINK SMARTER

Children will need to know how to recognize a model showing fourths. They should understand that the sizes of the four pieces of each model must be equal for the model to show fourths. Children who select the third answer choice likely are only counting the number of pieces, without considering whether those pieces are equal.

5 EVALUATE   Formative Assessment

Essential Question

Reflect Using the Language Objective Have children demonstrate and explain to answer the essential question.

How can drawing a diagram help when solving problems about equal shares?
Possible answer: I can draw to divide a shape in different ways to show halves, thirds, or fourths.

Math Journal    WRITE Math

Draw and write to explain how you can divide a rectangle into thirds in two different ways.

Practice and Homework

Use the Practice and Homework pages to provide children with more practice of the concepts and skills presented in this lesson. Children master their understanding as they complete practice items and then challenge their critical thinking skills with Problem Solving. Use the Write Math section to determine children's understanding of content for this lesson. Encourage children to use their Math Journals to record their answers.

Name _____

Problem Solving • Equal Shares

Practice and Homework
Lesson 11.11

 COMMON CORE STANDARD—2.G.A.3
Reason with shapes and their attributes.

Draw to show your answer. Check children's work. Possible answers are given.

1. Max has square pizzas that are the same size. What are two different ways he can divide the pizzas into fourths?

2. Lia has two pieces of paper that are the same size. What are two different ways she can divide the pieces of paper into halves?

3. **WRITE** ▸ Math Draw and write to explain how you can divide a rectangle into thirds in two different ways.

_____

Check children's work.

© Houghton Mifflin Harcourt Publishing Company

 **PROFESSIONAL DEVELOPMENT** **Math Talk in Action**

The class is discussing how to divide the squares in Exercise 1.

Teacher:	Into how many equal parts do you need to divide each square?
Will:	I need to divide each square into four equal parts.
Teacher:	How do you know?
Will:	The problem says to show fourths. Fourths means 4 equal parts.
Teacher:	What is one way you can divide the square?
Chase:	I can draw two lines across the shape.
Teacher:	Are there any other ways?

Lizzie:	Yes, I can draw a line up and down and a line from side to side.
Teacher:	Very good! How can we tell if all these ways are solutions to the problem?
Herga:	Well, we could draw each different way making sure we have shown equal parts and then count that there are 4 parts in each diagram.
Darren:	I can trace the squares and cut them out. Then I can cut each square into equal parts and put the parts on top of each other to see if all the parts are the same size.

Lesson Check (2.G.A.3)

1. Bree cut a piece of cardboard into thirds like this.

Circle the other shape that is divided into thirds.

Spiral Review (2.MD.C.7, 2.MD.A.3, 2.G.A.1)

2. Circle the shape with three equal parts.

3. How many angles does this shape have?

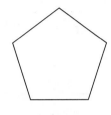

<u> 5 </u> angles

4. What is the best estimate for the length of a baseball bat?

Check children's estimates for reasonableness.

_____ feet

5. Which is another way to write 10 minutes after 9?

<u> 9 </u> : <u> 10 </u>

© Houghton Mifflin Harcourt Publishing Company

Continue concepts and skills practice with Lesson Check. Use Spiral Review to engage children in previously taught concepts and to promote content retention. Common Core standards are correlated to each section.

Summative Assessment

Use the **Chapter Review/Test** to assess children's progress in Chapter 11.

You may want to review with children the essential question for the chapter.

Chapter Essential Question

What are some two-dimensional shapes and three-dimensional shapes, and how can you show equal parts of shapes?

Ask the following questions to focus children's thinking:

- **How can you describe some two-dimensional and three-dimensional shapes?**
- **How can you describe equal parts of shapes?**

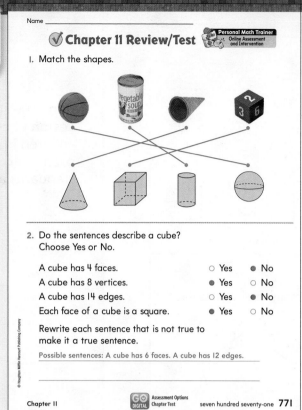

Name _____

✓ **Chapter 11 Review/Test**

Personal Math Trainer
Online Assessment and Intervention

1. Match the shapes.

2. Do the sentences describe a cube? Choose Yes or No.

A cube has 4 faces. ○ Yes ● No
A cube has 8 vertices. ● Yes ○ No
A cube has 14 edges. ○ Yes ● No
Each face of a cube is a square. ● Yes ○ No

Rewrite each sentence that is not true to make it a true sentence.
Possible sentences: A cube has 6 faces. A cube has 12 edges.

Chapter II   Assessment Options Chapter Test   seven hundred seventy-one **771**

3. Draw lines to show thirds.

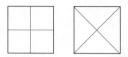

Explain how you know that the parts are thirds.
Possible answer: I drew lines to show 3 equal parts.

Each part is a third.

4. Will and Ana have gardens that are the same size. They each divide their gardens into fourths. What are two different ways they can divide the gardens? Draw to show your answer. Possible answers are shown.

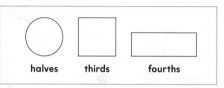

5. Draw to show halves, thirds, and fourths. Color a half of, a third of, and a fourth of the shape. Check children's work.

halves   thirds   fourths

772 seven hundred seventy-two

✓ Data-Driven Decision Making ▲ RtI Chapter II

Based on the results of the Chapter Review/Test use the following resources to review skills.

Item	Lesson	Standards	Content Focus	Personal Math Trainer	Intervene With
1	11.1	2.G.A.1	Match a three-dimensional shape to a real-world object.	2.G.A.1	R—11.1
2	11.2	2.G.A.1	Identify attributes of a cube.	2.G.A.1	R—11.2
3–5	11.9, 11.10, 11.11	2.G.A.3	Draw lines to show halves, thirds, and fourths.	2.G.A.3	R—11.9, 11.10, 11.11
6	11.7	2.G.A.2	Determine how many tiles are needed to cover a rectangle.	2.G.A.2	R—11.7
7	11.3	2.G.A.1	Determine how many cubes are needed to build a rectangular prism.	2.G.A.1	R—11.3
8, 9, 11	11.4, 11.5, 11.6	2.G.A.1	Recognize attributes of 2-dimensional shapes.	2.G.A.1	R—11.4, 11.5, 11.6
10	11.8	2.G.A.3	Identify shapes divided into fourths.	2.G.A.3	R—11.8

Key: R—Reteach (in the *Chapter Resources*)

6. Max wants to cover the rectangle with color tiles. Explain how you would estimate the number of square tiles he would need to cover the rectangle.

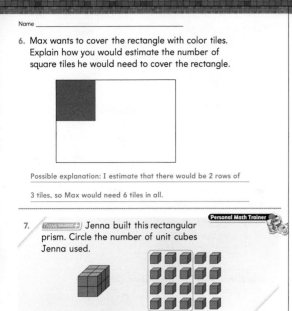

Possible explanation: I estimate that there would be 2 rows of

3 tiles, so Max would need 6 tiles in all.

7. **THINK SMARTER+**   **Personal Math Trainer**
Jenna built this rectangular prism. Circle the number of unit cubes Jenna used.

8. Rachel makes a pentagon and a quadrilateral with toothpicks. She uses one toothpick for each side of a shape. How many toothpicks does Rachel need?

_____9_____ toothpicks

9. Kevin drew 2 two-dimensional shapes that had 9 angles in all. Draw the shapes Kevin could have drawn. Check children's drawings.

10. Fill in the bubble next to the shapes that show fourths.

○   ●   ○   ●

11. **GO DEEPER**   Draw each shape where it belongs in the chart.

Shapes with fewer than 4 angles	Shapes with more than 3 Angles

Performance Assessment Tasks
Chapter 11

See the *Chapter Resources* for a Performance Task that assesses children's understanding of the content of this chapter.

For each task, you will find sample student work for each of the response levels in the task scoring rubric.

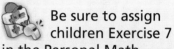 Performance Assessment Tasks may be used for portfolios.

Be sure to assign children Exercise 7 in the Personal Math Trainer. It features an animation or video to help children model and solve the problem.

Summative Assessment

Use the **Chapter Test** to assess children's progress in Chapter 11.

Chapter Tests are provided in Common Core assessment formats in the *Chapter Resources*.

Personal Math Trainer

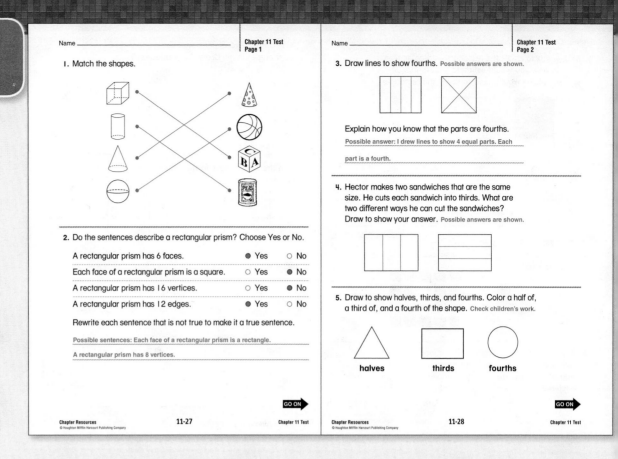

✓ Data-Driven Decision Making ▲ RtI

Based on the results of the Chapter Test use the following resources to review skills.

Item	Lesson	Standards	Content Focus	Personal Math Trainer	Intervene with
1	11.1	2.G.A.1	Match 3-dimensional shapes to real-world objects.	2.G.A.1	R—11.1
2	11.2	2.G.A.1	Identify attributes of a rectangular prism.	2.G.A.1	R—11.2
3–5	11.9, 11.10, 11.11	2.G.A.3	Draw lines to show halves, thirds, and fourths.	2.G.A.3	R—11.9, 11.10, 11.11
6	11.7	2.G.A.2	Determine how many tiles are needed to cover a rectangle.	2.G.A.2	R—11.7
7	11.3	2.G.A.1	Determine how many cubes are needed to build a rectangular prism.	2.G.A.1	R—11.3
8, 9, 11	11.4, 11.5, 11.6	2.G.A.1	Recognize attributes of 2-dimensional shapes.	2.G.A.1	R—11.4, 11.5, 11.6
10	11.8	2.G.A.3	Identify shapes divided into thirds.	2.G.A.3	R—11.8

Key: R—Reteach (in the *Chapter Resources*)

6. Grace wants to cover the rectangle with gray tiles.
Explain how you would estimate the number of
gray tiles she would need to cover the rectangle.

Possible explanation: I estimate that there would be 2 rows

of 4 tiles, so Grace would need 8 tiles in all.

7. Alex built this rectangular prism. Circle the
number of unit cubes Alex used.

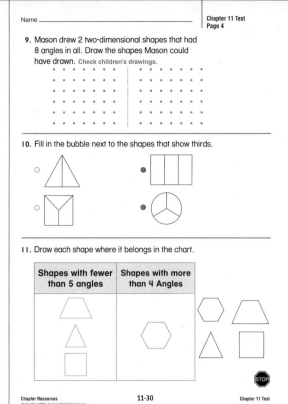

8. Paul makes a hexagon and a triangle with straws.
He uses one straw for each side of a shape. How
many straws does Paul need?

_____9_____ straws

GO ON

9. Mason drew 2 two-dimensional shapes that had
8 angles in all. Draw the shapes Mason could
have drawn. Check children's drawings.

10. Fill in the bubble next to the shapes that show thirds.

11. Draw each shape where it belongs in the chart.

Shapes with fewer than 5 angles	Shapes with more than 4 Angles

STOP

Portfolio Suggestions

The portfolio represents the growth, talents, achievements, and reflections of the mathematics learner. Children might spend a short time selecting work samples for their portfolios.

You may want to have children respond to the following questions:

- How do you think you did on this test?
- What do you understand about the chapter that you did not understand before the chapter?
- What would you like to learn more about?

For information about how to organize, share, and evaluate portfolios, see the *Chapter Resources.*

Chapter 11 Test

Chapter 11 Test   774B